WORKBOOK

for use with

BASIC BUSINESS COMMUNICATION

Sixth Edition

Raymond V. Lesikar
John D. Pettit, Jr.
both of University of North Texas
Marie E. Flatley
San Diego State University

IRWIN
Homewood, IL 60430
Boston, MA 02116

©Richard D. Irwin, Inc., 1979, 1982, 1985, 1988, 1991, and 1993

Printer in the United Staes of America.

ISBN 0-256-11059-X

1 2 3 4 5 6 7 8 9 0 VK 9 8 7 6 5 4 3 2

Contents

Some Basic Introductory Words

1

Multiple Choice (Circle the best answer)

1. The members of a business organization who usually communicate most in their daily work activities are the
    a. top administrators.
    b. maintenance workers.
    c. middle-level managers.
    d. production workers.
    e. accountants.

2. A memorandum sent by a worker in the sales department of Company X to workers in the production department of Company X listing specifications of a product to be built for a customer would be classified as:
    a. external-operational communication.
    b. internal-operational communication.
    c. personal communication.
    d. grapevine communication.
    e. expository communication.

3. A salesperson's presentation to a customer would be classified as:
    a. external-operational communication.
    b. internal-operational communication.
    c. personal communication.
    d. grapevine communication.
    e. expository communication.

4. The flow of operational communications in an organization should be
    a. stopped, if possible.
    b. downward only.
    c. upward only.
    d. upward and downward.
    e. lateral only.

5. Best advice for a manager concerning how to deal with the grapevine is to:
    a. eliminate it.
    b. keep in touch with it and use it.
    c. ignore it.
    d. convert it into a formal network.
    e. ridicule it at every opportunity.

6. How much communicating is done in a business depends on:
    a. the nature of the business.
    b. the operating plan of the business
    c. the people in the business.
    d. all of the items above.
    e. management's control over the grapevine.

7. You do not detect everything in your sensory world because:
   a. your senses are limited.
   b. your mental alertness is not always keen.
   c. you tune out some of it.
   d. all of the above.
   e. your mental filter is unique.

8. The meaning you give a message is determined by:
   a. your mental filter (your experience, knowledge, biases, emotions).
   b. your personality and character.
   c. dictionary definitions.
   d. your imagination.
   e. your senses (eyes, ears, and such).

9. In the description of the communication process presented in the chapter, a communication response may consist of
   a. written words only.
   b. spoken words only.
   c. gestures, written words, and spoken words only.
   d. physical actions only.
   e. any of the communication forms named above.

10. One of the following statements describes one of the three significant differences between written and oral communication. Mark it.
    a. Oral communication has longer times between cycles.
    b. Written communication is more likely to be a creative effort.
    c. Oral communication involves a more limited number of cycles.
    d. Written communication involves symbols whereas oral communication does not.
    e. Oral communication is more exact.

Completion

1. The higher you advance in business, the _____ you are likely to communicate.

2. Communication is essential to the organized effort involved in business because _____
   _____ .

3. Internal-operational communication is defined as _____
   _____
   _____ .

4. As a result of progress in technoloy, much of the internal-operational communication in business is done using _____ .

5. External-operational communication is defined as _____
   _____
   _____
   _____ .

6. The major reason why words do not accurately describe reality is that _____
   _____ .

7. Fitting the message to the reader (using words they understand) is called _____. It is important to communication because communication suffers unless the words _____
_____.

8. Analysis of the communication process brings out three underlying truths: (1) _____
(2) _____,
(3) _____.

Application Exercises

1. Classify each of the following communication incidents by the three forms of communication in the organization (internal-operational, external-operational, and personal):
   a. A company salesperson receives a telephone call from a customer who complains about a product.
   b. The supervisor of a production department reports the details of an accident by sending a memorandum to the safety officer.
   c. Two workers on a production line discuss possibilities that their union leaders will call a strike.
   d. A supervisor stops to talk with a worker on an assembly line to inquire about the status of the worker's sick child.
   e. An employee in a purchasing department prepares and mails an order for goods needed to maintain inventory levels.
   f. The president of a company addresses a civic organization in the community.

2. Using the communication process described in the book as a guide, analyze the following dialogue. Your analysis should point out and explain the miscommunication involved.

   Old Worker: "They tell me a union is trying to take over this place. When that happens, I'll quit."

   Young Worker: "Don't worry, pops. That wouldn't be bad."

   Old Worker: "Don't tell me about unions, son. I've worked around them for over 30 years—even belonged to one once. They're bad—real bad."

   Young Worker: "That's not a fair statement. They've done a lot of good. We've got better salaries, better benefits, and better working conditions because of them."

   Old Worker: "You've been brainwashed by the communist-controlled press and those left-wing professors. You liberals are taking this country to ruin."

   Young Worker: "Liberal! I just happen to believe in supporting what's best for the people. It's hard-line conservatives like you who are ruining us."

   From this point on the disagreements accelerated, leading to exchanges of insults emphasized by four-letter words.

Adaptation and the Selection of Words

2

Multiple Choice (Circle the best answer)

1. The first step in *adapting* your message to the reader is:
   a. deciding what kind of vocabulary to use.
   b. deciding on the company goal to be served.
   c. forming a mental picture of what the reader is like.
   d. researching the situation about which the reader wants to know.
   e. outlining the logical developments of the message.

2. In adapting to the reader you will need to consider:
   a. the reader's knowledge of the subject.
   b. the reader's educational level.
   c. the reader's vocabulary.
   d. how the reader thinks.
   e. all of the above.

3. For best results in getting the message across to the reader you should:
   a. expect the reader to adjust to your normal writing if you know the subject well.
   b. follow the company policy manual's writing style.
   c. try to impress the reader with a large vocabulary.
   d. select words easily understood by the intended reader.
   e. always write on a level lower than you are.

4. Adapting to the reader supports the use of a writing style that:
   a. stresses simplicity in word choices.
   b. uses big words, as Winston Churchill suggested.
   c. impresses with knowledge of the subject.
   d. suggests the reader has a sophisticated vocabulary.
   e. suggests the reader knows as much as the writer about the subject.

5. Research supports the idea that the writing level that communicates best is:
   a. the highest level a reader can understand.
   b. the average level a reader can understand.
   c. a level slightly below the reader's level of understanding.
   d. a level slightly below the writer's level of understanding.
   e. no important research has been done on the subject.

6. In selecting words for clear communication, prefer/choose:
   a. familiar words.
   b. everyday words.
   c. clear words.
   d. shorter words.
   e. all of the above.

7. Technical words:
   a. are useful when communicating with people in your field.
   b. impress others with your knowledge.
   c. are widely understood.
   d. should never be used.
   e. are seldom understood except by college graduates.

8. Avoid:
   a. using only short words.
   b. using many long words.
   c. using technical words with people outside your field.
   d. using formal legal language.
   e. all of the above.

9. In choosing words to build a sentence, remember that the strongest part of speech is the:
   a. noun.
   b. pronoun.
   c. verb.
   d. adverb.
   e. adjective.

10. Concrete words are the *opposite* of words that are:
    a. soft.
    b. vague.
    c. specific.
    d. short.
    e. technical.

11. Changing a verb (action word) into the subject (noun) in a sentence:
    a. gets more movement into the sentence.
    b. makes a stronger sentence since the verb is the strongest part of speech.
    c. makes effective use of the active voice.
    d. results in a longer sentence using a passive voice.
    e. gets directly to the point of the sentence.

12. In adapting your message to multiple readers, you need to:
    a. write at a high level so as not to insult the best educated.
    b. write using technical terms so as not to insult those who know most about the subject.
    c. adapt to the lowest level you need to reach.
    d. adapt your style to the middle, or "average," members of the group.
    e. assume none of the readers knows anything about the subject.

13. For effective business writing the following combination is best:
    a. concrete words and active verbs.
    b. abstract words and active verbs.
    c. concrete words and passive verbs.
    d. abstract words and passive verbs.
    e. short words and camouflaged verbs.

14. Precise use of words in business writing requires:
    a. awareness of shades of difference in meanings of similar words.
    b. awareness of correct use of idioms.
    c. use of persons and things instead of action words as the subject of the sentence.
    d. a good dictionary.
    e. all of the above.

15. Which of the following sentences would be least likely to offend a member of a minority group?
    a. We hired a hard-working black man.
    b. Maria will represent the hispanic members.
    c. For a Baptist she is broad-minded.
    d. He was an honest Italian.
    e. Jack is an intelligent Irishman.

16. Which of these sentences contains the least sexist wording?
    a. She is the best lady lawyer in town.
    b. All city policemen must take the test.
    c. If a person tries, he can succeed.
    d. If students study, they will pass.
    e. Our advertisement for a salesman stressed that we are an equal-opportunity employer.

17. Mark the sentence that uses words that are most likely *not* to offend old or young people.
    a. The waiting room was filled with senior citizens.
    b. Today's teenagers are unable to cope with this problem.
    c. The new president is the typical grandfatherly type.
    d. Many of the young people at the meeting objected to the ruling.
    e. You old timers may not understand why we must take this action.

18. Mark the word that is least discriminatory toward people with disabilities.
    a. Deaf
    b. Crippled
    c. Retarded
    d. Dumb
    e. Hearing impaired

Completion

1. *Adaptation* in writing means _____ the message to the _____
_____.

2. In adapting to multiple readers, you need to write to the _____ level you need to reach.

3. Verbs are the strongest part of speech because they are _____ words.

4. In good business writing, adjectives and adverbs should be used _____.

5. Words that are specific or exact are _____, and words that are vague and general are_____.

6. Stronger, livelier writing results from using the _____ voice because it places more emphasis on the _____.

7. "The football was caught by the quarterback" is an example of the _____ voice, and "The quarterback caught the ball" is an example of the _____ voice.

8. "Alice wrote the report" is an example of _____ voice; "The report was written by Alice," _____ voice.

9. "The acquisition of a new computer was realized by the company" uses a(n) _____ as a subject and the _____ voice in the verb.

10. It will help you avoid using camouflaged verbs as nouns if you make the subject of most sentences _____ or _____ .

11. The normal order of a sentence is 1st _____, 2nd _____, and 3rd _____, with the subject being the _____ _____ _____ _____.

12. _____ is the way ideas are expressed and the way we say things in our language.

13. To be precise in your writing you need to be aware of the _____ in meanings of similar words.

14. Clear writing is built on a foundation of (a) _____ and (b) _____.

15. Discriminatory words are defined as words that _____ _____.

16. You can avoid using the masculine pronouns *he*, *him*, or *his* to designate both sexes in three ways:
    (1) _____
    (2) _____
    (3) _____

Application Exercises

Using the suggestions in Chapter 2, edit the following sentences so they communicate more clearly and easily and precisely. If any are in passive voice, change them to active voice.

1. The utilization of natural resources in close proximity to the plant could reduce operating costs.

2. Modification of the initial design was responsible for increased efficiency.

3. Can you substantiate that statement?

4. Let me enumerate the causes.

5. The glutinous substance subsequently modified the predisposition of the formula to coagulate.

6. The machine is inoperative; we must ascertain the cause.

7. I am hoping for an increase in my reimbursement.

8. The new procedure was inaugurated last month.

9. It would be erroneous to assume that an increment in the aggregate should cause disintegration if the pressures fluctuated.

10. Are you cognizant of the optimum level of utilization?

11. Please send your remittance in the enclosed envelope.

12. The writing style obfuscated comprehension of the results.

13. It is obligatory to fill out the forms initially.

14. What is your proximity to the metropolis?

15. In recapitulating the paramount points of adaptation, let me stress the exigency of avoiding obtuse words.

16. The wave obliterated the words written in the sand.

17. The fire caused a lot of damage to my office.

18. Please ship the merchandise for the sale soon.

19. Heretofore the reports were submitted by us before September 17.

20. The subsequent plan was superior than the initial one.

Construction of Clear Sentences and Paragraphs

3

Multiple Choice (Circle the best answer)

1. Sentences, like words, should be adapted to the reader's:
   a. knowledge of the subject.
   b. education.
   c. intelligence.
   d. b and c.
   e. a, b, and c.

2. Your reader will comprehend sentences most easily that are written at a level:
   a. challenging to the reader.
   b. impressive to the reader.
   c. appropriate to the technical expertise of the writer.
   d. above the reader.
   e. a little below the level of the reader.

3. Writing that is readable for the middle-level or adult reader should average around _____ words per sentence.
   a. 5–8
   b. 9–12
   c. 13–15
   d. 16–18
   e. 19–24

4. For clearer communication, you should:
   a. always use short sentences.
   b. never use complex sentences.
   c. be concerned with the average sentence length.
   d. always use longer sentences for subordinate information.
   e. not worry about the sentence length if you use short words.

5. To get in the habit of writing short sentences, you should:
   a. limit sentence content.
   b. present several simple ideas.
   c. use only short words.
   d. eliminate transitions.
   e. use only active verbs.

6. Thought units:
   a. should always be limited to one to a sentence.
   b. may occasionally be combined in a sentence.
   c. should be connected by appropriate conjunctions (*and, but*) to keep a series of simple ideas together in a sentence.
   d. should not be separated by periods if they are on a single topic.
   e. are sentences you have not written down yet.

7. To write clearer, more readable sentences:
   a. avoid cluttering phrases.
   b. eliminate surplus words that add nothing.
   c. write directly to the point.
   d. avoid repetition unless used for emphasis or special effect.
   e. all of the above.

8. For a sentence to have unity, all of its parts must:
   a. work together to form one clear thought.
   b. follow the subject-verb-object construction.
   c. have both independent and dependent clauses.
   d. have parts of equal strength.
   e. include as much detail as possible.

9. Confused meaning can result from:
   a. dangling modifiers.
   b. subject-verb disagreement.
   c. pronouns that do not clearly identify preceding nouns.
   d. unclear thinking.
   e. all of the above.

10. A paragraph should:
    a. consist of at least three sentences.
    b. build around a single topic or idea.
    c. include several different ideas or topics.
    d. have both simple and complex sentences.
    e. never be longer than eight lines.

11. A paragraph should:
    a. help make ideas stand out.
    b. show the reader where topics begin and end.
    c. have unity.
    d. be short most of the time.
    e. all of the above.

12. One-line paragraphs:
    a. should never be used.
    b. can be used to emphasize a major point.
    c. should be used frequently.
    d. are good for subordinating content.
    e. give the writing sophistication.

13. The topic sentence of a paragraph:
    a. should always come first in the paragraph.
    b. should be in the middle of the paragraph.
    c. should be last to summarize the paragraph.
    d. may vary in location depending on the paragraph.
    e. should be preceded by an independent clause.

14. Identify the best plan for clear writing:
    a. precise words, compound sentences, single-topic paragraphs.
    b. familiar words, short sentences, paragraphs with unity.
    c. abstract words, short sentences, paragraphs with unity.
    d. long words, short sentences, compound paragraphs.
    e. short words, long sentences, dual-topic sentences in paragraphs.

15. Identify the topic sentence in the example paragraph in the last section of Chapter 3 in the textbook (p. 67). It is about:
    a. three reasons.
    b. building rock in the Crowton area.
    c. the failure of recent geological explorations.
    d. distances from Crowton to major consumption areas.
    e. the obsolescence of much of the equipment at the Crowton plant.

Completion

1. In writing to less informed and less educated readers, you should concentrate on _____ sentence design; you may use more _____ designs in writing to more knowledgeable and better educated readers.

2. If you put many words or many relationships in a sentence, you increase the possibility of _____ _____.

3. Longer sentences sometimes are useful in _____ information.

4. Two techniques for writing simple, short sentences are: first, _____ and, second, _____ _____.

5. A sentence is more apt to be simple and short if you try to use _____ thought units per sentence.

6. "Economizing on words" means consciously _____.

7. Two ways of economizing on words are to avoid (a) _____ and (b) _____.

8. The expression "In my opinion I think" is an example of_____.

9. A _____ sentence carries more emphasis than a(n) _____ one.

10. If you have two ideas in a sentence, you can emphasize one and give less importance to the second by putting the less important in a(n) _____ clause and the more important in a(n) _____ clause.

11. Using all short sentences gives each sentence _____ emphasis and gives a _____ _____ in reading.

12. Selection of points for emphasis is the responsibility of_____.

13. Three ways of destroying unity in a paragraph are: (a) _____, (b) _____, and (c)_____.

14. "While reading the report, a gust of wind blew the papers off my desk" is an example of a(n) _____ _____, which confuses meaning by modifying the wrong word.

15. A paragraph should be built around _____ in order to have unity.

Application Exercises

Identify the major problem of each of the following sentences (see problem list), and correct/edit it for greater readability.

Problems include
a. cluttering phrase
b. surplus words
c. roundabout construction
d. unnecessary repetition
e. unrelated ideas

_____ 1. In the near future a new policy will replace the present plan.

_____ 2. In the event that the shipment is not received on time, it will be impossible to meet our monthly quota.

_____ 3. It is essential that the report be turned in on time.

_____ 4. It is advisable that instructors should take appropriate action to determine whether students are attending classes regularly.

_____ 5. Meeting the demand is impossible at the present time.

_____ 6. It is observable that in the most common paragraph plans, supporting material follows the topic sentence.

_____ 7. It is important to notice that good report writing has movement.

_____ 8. The meeting will be at 2:30 p.m. tomorrow in the afternoon.

_____ 9. Action taken at the present time will afford the committee an opportunity to finish sooner than if we wait until next week.

_____ 10. By the time that April 1 arrives, the company hopes to have made an acquisition of the adjacent land for expansion.

_____ 11. Her letter reported a gain to the effect of a 23 percent increase in production.

_____ 12. The report was due Monday, and it was about possible new plan sites.

_____ 13. Estimates must be in the neighborhood of the amount we have budgeted for repairs.

_____ 14. We rejected the plan for the reason that it required more time than we had.

_____ 15. In the event that the shipment is not received by October 29, we will make a cancellation for the new machinery.

_____ 16. A topic sentence expresses the main idea of a paragraph, and one may be at the beginning, middle, or end.

_____ 17. There are two basic techniques that will help one to write in short, simple sentences.

_____ 18. In your opinion do you think that more evening classes should be offered?

Writing for Effect

4

Multiple Choice (Circle the best answer)

1. Writing in a conversational style:
   a. means using warm and natural language.
   b. means writing the way we talk.
   c. helps us avoid the big word and the difficult word.
   d. helps us avoid dull and stiff wordage.
   e. all of the above.

2. A "rubber stamp" is:
   a. a way of being extra polite that is based on the language of the old nobility.
   b. an expression that suggests to the reader he/she is being dealt with routinely.
   c. an expression borrowed from legal language that is meant to make the writing extremely precise.
   d. one of a special group of expressions considered desirable to quickly identify specific letter situations.
   e. a stamp with the boss's signature on it used by a secretary to "sign" letters to give them that "personal touch."

3. The effect of goodwill is most likely to be achieved in your writing through use of:
   a. formality.
   b. rubber stamps.
   c. repetition.
   d. the "language of business."
   e. a conversational style.

4. Writing from the you-viewpoint means:
   a. making the reader feel the writer really cares by using personal pronouns such as *I* and *we* and *us*.
   b. choosing words skillfully to stress the writer's (and the company's) point of view.
   c. viewing the situation from the reader's point of view rather than the writer's.
   d. using only *you* and *your* pronouns.
   e. telling customers/readers what they want to hear.

5. The you-viewpoint technique is suitable for:
   a. good-news letters.
   b. bad-news letters.
   c. persuasive letters.
   d. advertising copy.
   e. all of the above.

6. Words that can create reader resistance and destroy goodwill include:
   a. those with negative connotations.
   b. those that convey meanings of unhappy and unpleasant events.
   c. words that deny.
   d. words that sound unpleasant.
   e. all types listed above.

7. As you work to achieve the goal of communicating courtesy:
   a. write to give the specific situation individual treatment.
   b. let the reader know you are giving the benefit of superior knowledge.
   c. impress the reader with sincerity by "telling it like it is."
   d. use expressions such as "*you* need" and "*you* must" for the you-effect.
   e. all of the above.

8. The goodwill effect can be best served:
   a. if you sincerely want to be sincere and want to treat your reader's feelings with tact.
   b by referring to your reader by name in each sentence.
   c. by using superlative "est" words for emphasis.
   d. if you sincerely express whatever your real feelings are.
   e. all of the above.

9. In the letter you are writing, you have some good news you want to emphasize. Put it:
   a. in the first 5-8 words of the first sentence.
   b. in the middle of the first paragraph.
   c. in the first sentence of the middle paragraph.
   d. in the middle of the middle paragraph.
   e. at the beginning of the last paragraph.

10. In the letter you are writing, you must tell the reader some bad news; you want to de-emphasize the negative part of the message. Put the bad news:
    a. in the first 5-8 words of the first sentence.
    b. in the middle of the first paragraph.
    c. in the first sentence of the middle paragraph.
    d. in the middle of the middle paragraph.
    e. at the beginning of the last paragraph.

11. Techniques of mechanical emphasis include:
    a. underscoring and italics.
    b. quotation marks and capital letters.
    c. color.
    d. drawings.
    e. all of the above.

12. You are answering a claim letter from a customer who reported receiving damaged merchandise. A good first sentence might be:
    a. We regret to hear that the merchandise you received was broken.
    b. You have the right to be upset about the broken items.
    c. Three new cases of a replacement shipment are being rushed to you by express mail.
    d. We will replace the damaged cases of raspberry jam at once.
    e. Calm down! Everyone makes mistakes!

13. A job applicant failed the typing test. You must notify her or him, but you wish to be tactful. Which sentence best meets the goal?
   a. We regret to tell you that your typing score was too low.
   b. Unfortunately, you made too many errors on the typing test.
   c. Your sloppy typing makes a bad impression.
   d. You failed to meet our required score.
   e. Your score on the typing test was 25 words; the speed required for the job is 60 words.

14. You are sending a potential customer a catalog he or she asked for. The best of these opening sentences for your letter is:
   a. I am happy to be able to answer your letter.
   b. I have received your letter asking for the catalog.
   c. This will acknowledge receipt of your June 10th letter.
   d. Enclosed is the catalog on our decorator lamps.
   e. In accordance with your instructions, we are happy to enclose our last catalog on decorator lamps.

Completion

1. When you write letters, you need to communicate both _____ and _____.

2. Words or expressions used by habit in a letter every time a certain type of situation occurs are called _____.

3. Writing from the you-viewpoint means emphasizing _____ interests and concerns.

4. _____ words are more apt to create the goodwill atmosphere in a letter, while _____ words may stir resistance and destroy goodwill.

5. Two ways of making your reader feel singled out for special consideration are _____ and _____.

6. Using angry or sarcastic words and expressions is apt to serve only the doubtful "goal" of _____.

7. Four major techniques of emphasizing an idea in a letter or report are (a) _____, (b) _____, (c) _____, and (d) _____.

8. For emphasis purposes, the strongest points of a paragraph or letter are _____ and _____.

9. In constructing a paragraph and using techniques of length for emphasis, put the most important information in _____ sentences and supporting information in _____ sentences.

10. Words or phrases that bridge or tie together the various bits of information contained in a letter or report are known as _____.

11. Your letters are made up of both (a) independent bits of information and (b) _____.

12. Four major transitional devices are (a) _____, (b) _____, (c) _____, and (d) _____.

13. An example of a transitional word that suggests a contrast in ideas is _____, while a transitional word that suggests similarity is _____.

Application Exercises

Identify the major errors in the following paragraphs.

Example 1:

(1) (2) (3)

This will acknowledge receipt of your letter of December 8, in which you *claim* to have received a *damaged* shipment

(4) (5)

from us. I am *sorry* to hear that the bottles of lotion were such a *sticky, gooey* mess when you got them. *In accordance*

(6) (7)

with your instructions on said matter, we have sent a replacement shipment, which should reach you *soon.* Probably if

(8)

your employees had been *less careless* when unpacking the shipment, some of the bottles still would have been usable,

(9) (10)

but to *show our goodwill* we are replacing the entire three cases. *We trust this will meet with your favor.* Again, we

(11) (12)

regret the breakage. Looking forward to receiving your next order, we remain

1.
2.
3.
4.
5.
6.
7.
8.
9.
10.
11.
12.

Example 2:

(1) (2)

You must take advantage of our introductory offer on our new line of male cosmetics. *Already thousands of satisfied*

(3)

customers are writing to tell us of the *stupendous* improvement in their social lives after using Sinbad toiletries.

(4) (5)

I know you will want to take advantage of the 15% discount on orders placed within 10 days on this *fantastic* new line.

(6) (7)

Hoping to receive your immediate response, *I remain yours truly,*

1.
2.
3.
4.
5.
6.
7.

Example 3:

                       (1)   (2)   (3)

I am happy to be able to answer your letter about our dependable See-Brite lamps. *I assure* you, you will *never* have to   (4)   (5)
worry about a *failure* with See-Brite products. Let one of our lamps be the *brightest* spot in your home. *Find enclosed*   (6)
herewith the catalog you requested.

1.
2.
3.
4.
5.
6.

Example 4:

           (1)   (2)   (3)

If you had read the instruction book enclosed with the shelving set, *you would not have made the mistake* in assembling   (4)   (5)
the shelves about which you wrote *in your letter of September 12*. You *failed* to properly connect sections M and N, or   (6)
the shelves *would not have collapsed* as you claimed.

           (7)

You must follow the instructions to insure the dependable service for which Stay-Put storage units are known. *If we*   (8)   (9)
can be of any further assistance, just let us know. *Your satisfaction is our goal.*

1.
2.
3.
4.
5.
6.
7.
8.
9.

Directness in Initiating Routine Letters

5

Multiple Choice (Circle the best answer)

1. In a direct letter plan, you should begin with:
    a.   introductory remarks.
    b.   identification of the situation to which you are responding.
    c.   the objective.
    d.   explanatory remarks.
    e.   information about the reason for writing.

2. Of the following, the best way to begin a routine inquiry letter is with:
    a.   a question.
    b.   a compliment.
    c.   an informational statement.
    d.   a goodwill comment.
    e.   explanation.

3. As a hobbyist with a home workshop, you want information about a new circular saw you read about in a home-improvements column in a popular magazine. A good opening sentence in a letter to the manufacturer would be:
    a.   I read about your new circular saw in the home-improvements section of the August *Home* magazine.
    b.   Would you please send me a descriptive brochure about your circular saw Model No. 4-217?
    c.   Please tell me something about your circular saw Model No. 4-217.
    d.   The August *Home* magazine had an article about home workshops that talked about your new Model No. 4-217 circular saw.
    e.   I have a home workshop and was wondering if your Model No. 4-217 circular saw described on page 82 of the August issue of *Home* magazine would meet my needs.

4. Your business leases and services washing machines and dryers in several apartment buildings. You are considering buying a microcomputer to help you in record keeping. A good first sentence for a letter seeking information would be:
    a.   My business leases and services washing machines and dryers in several apartment buildings.
    b.   I am considering buying a microcomputer to use with my business.
    c.   I am considering buying a microcomputer for record keeping in my business.
    d.   Tell me something about microcomputers and record keeping in a small business.
    e.   Do you lease microcomputers to small businesses in this area?

5. These are five steps that usually are involved in writing a good-news letter:
    1. begin directly
    2. identify your goal
    3. explain
    4. close with goodwill
    5. determine how you think the reader will react to your goal

   Mark the order in which they should occur.
    a. 1–2–3–4–5.
    b. 1–2–5–3–4.
    c. 2–5–1–3–4.
    d. 2–1–5–3–4.
    e. 5–2–1–3–4.

6. A good way to make questions stand out is to:
    a. have only one question in a sentence.
    b. have only one question in a paragraph.
    c. number your questions when there are more than one.
    d. write your questions as questions, not statements.
    e. all of the above.

7. A good place for explanation in an inquiry letter is:
    a. in the first sentence.
    b. after the first sentence.
    c. in a paragraph by itself.
    d. in the closing paragraph.
    e. any of the above is OK.

8. In a closing paragraph in a routine inquiry letter, you should have:
    a. a question.
    b. an explanation.
    c. a promise to buy.
    d. a friendly comment.
    e. any of the above is OK.

9. The best close to the letter suggested in Question 4 would be:
    a. Since I am interested in updating my office procedures soon, I'll appreciate having the information on your XY computer in the next week.
    b. A prompt reply will be appreciated.
    c. Thank you in advance for your answer to my inquiry.
    d. Hoping to receive the information quickly, I remain.
    e. all of the above are OK.

10. Inquiries about people:
    a. follow generally the same pattern as claim letters.
    b. must respect certain moral and legal rights.
    c. should seek the reader's opinion.
    d. should always ask about the applicant's personality.
    e. should begin indirectly with explanation.

11. In writing an inquiry about a job applicant, you should:
    a. analyze the job first.
    b. analyze the applicant first.
    c. begin with an explanation of job requirements.
    d. begin with a promise of confidentiality.
    e. begin with an off-subject, pleasant comment.

12. Letters about job applicants:
    a. should begin indirectly with explanation.
    b. should cover the applicant's qualifications to do the job.
    c. are best written as routine form letters.
    d. differ from routine inquiry letters by closing with a question.
    e. do not differ from routine inquiry letters in any way.

13. In a bad-news situation:
    a. indirect order is appropriate.
    b. begin with a direct statement of the problem.
    c. a direct subject line is appropriate.
    d. you can forget the goodwill in the close.
    e. you should tell the reader what you want her or his company to do and where to go.

14. In a claim letter situation:
    a. use an indirect approach since it is a bad-news situation.
    b. identify quickly what the claim is about.
    c. cover the identification of the situation in the middle paragraph.
    d. use anger to emphasize your loss.
    e. always leave the adjustment up to the reader.

15. An order letter should begin with:
    a. the identifying facts.
    b. a description of the goods you are ordering.
    c. a clear authorization to ship the goods.
    d. a subject line.
    e. a friendly comment.

Completion

1. Your first step in the process of writing a business letter should involve _____.

2. You should begin planning a letter by determining the _____.

3. After you determined the objective of your letter, you next predict_____
   _____.

4. If you predict you reader will react positively, or neutrally, generally you should organize the letter in
   _____ order.

5. If you predict your reader will react negatively, usually you should organize the letter in the _____
   _____ order.

6. Although time pressures may prevent you from doing it when you write letters in business, while you are in a learning situation as you are in this class you can improve your work by (1)_____, (2)_____, and (3) _____ _____.

7. If you have several questions to ask in a routine inquiry letter, you may begin your letter with either a(n) _____ or a(n) _____ question.

8. Taking a general question to start your letter allows you to ask specific questions in a _____ _____.

9. If your reader needs information to answer your questions, you need to include _____.

10. Two places to include information for your reader in an inquiry letter are (a) _____ and (b) _____.

11. The last paragraph of a routine inquiry letter should include_____.

12. For the best goodwill results, the closing comment should be _____.

13. A routine inquiry about people differs from a routine inquiry about a product because it needs to _____ _____.

14. You should ask for information about a person ONLY when _____.

15. You should tell the reader that information about a person will be held in _____.

16. A bad-news letter type that responds to direct letter treatment is the _____ letter.

17. When you use a subject line to identify a situation, it usually appears _____.

Application Exercises

You are director of training for the Galaxy Chemical Company. At last month's meeting of the Training Directors Association, one of the directors present told you about an excellent training film titled *Management and General Semantics*. This film is sold by Management Training Needs, Inc., a new company in the training-aids area. You would like to know more about the film, so you decide to write the company.

Although you would appreciate any information Management Training Needs can give you about the film, you certainly will want to know its cost, both rental and outright purchase. Also, you'd like to know its length, in minutes, as well as the general nature of its contents. You'd also like to know the level of audience (top executives, supervisors, workers) at which the film aims.

1. Arrange the following topics to form an outline of the letter you would write for this problem:
   a. expression of gratitude for assistance.
   b. specific question about cost.
   c. general request for the information needed.
   d. specific questions about audience level.
   e. explanation of situation.
   Sequence:____c____, ____e____, ____d____, ____b____, and ____a____.

2. Which of the following sentences would make the best opening for this letter?
    a. We are interested in knowing more about your film *Management and General Semantics*.
    b. Will you please answer the following questions about your film *Management and General Semantics*?
    c. We hear excellent reports about your film *Management and General Semantics*.
    d. This is to inquire about one of your management-training films.
    e. At last month's meeting, one of the directors of our company told us about your film *Management and General Semantics*.

3. In this problem, numbering and listing the questions would:
    a. be appropriate.
    b. not be appropriate.

4. Which of the following sentences is best for getting information concerning purchase cost?
    a. We would like to know how much the film costs.
    b. What are (1) the rental cost and (2) the purchase cost of the film?
    c. We need to know the cost of the film.
    d. Will you please give us the information we need, including level of audience, cost (rental and purchase), contents, and length of the film?

5. An appropriate close for this letter might be:
    a. Your prompt reply will be appreciated.
    b. We appreciate your attention to this situation.
    c. We look forward to considering your film for possible inclusion in our management-training program.
    d. We appreciate your answering our questions about your film.
    e. Thanking you in advance for the information about the film, we remain.

6. What is the goal of this letter?

    To get information.

7. What is the reader's reaction likely to be to this goal?

    Give information. Answer questions.

8. Now write your own inquiry letter requesting information about the film.

Directness in Routine Responses

6

Multiple Choice (Circle the best answer)

1. In answering an inquiry letter favorably, the first thing you want to do is:
    a. acknowledge receipt of the reader's letter.
    b. thank the reader for the inquiry.
    c. identify the correspondence being answered.
    d. be genuinely cordial.
    e. answer the reader's questions.

2. Since you want to emphasize the good news in the reply letter, you'll want to put it:
    a. at the beginning.
    b. in the middle.
    c. at the end.
    d. after an explanation.
    e. in a long sentence.

3. The best of these beginnings for a reply to the inquiry letter in the application exercise for Chapter 5, page 24 is:
    a. Here are the answers to your questions on the film *Management and General Semantics* as requested in your June 17th letter.
    b. We're delighted to hear of your interest in our film *Management and General Semantics.*
    c. We are glad to be able to answer your letter of June 17th.
    d. Thank you for your inquiry about the film *Management and General Semantics.*
    e. We believe our film *Management and General Semantics*, about which you inquired in your July 17th letter, is one of the best training films on the market for the cost.

4. If you need to provide answers to several questions in your reply letter, one way is to:
    a. answer them all immediately in the first paragraph.
    b. answer them all in the middle paragraph for convenience and compactness.
    c. make the answers stand out clearly by putting them in separate paragraphs.
    d. start with the explanation and then number the answers.
    e. use a separate line to identify each separate answer.

5. If your reply contains both good news and bad news, handle the bad news by:
    a. putting it at the beginning of the letter.
    b. putting it at the end of the letter.
    c. putting it at the beginning or end of the middle paragraph.
    d. placing it in a position of little emphasis.
    e. covering it thoroughly to be convincing.

6. An effective favorable reply letter:
    a. begins by telling what the reader wants to hear.
    b. answers all questions in a logical order.
    c. includes extra comments or suggestions showing an interest in a reader's problem.
    d. adapts a cordial close to the one situation.
    e. all of the above.

7. Acknowledgment letters:
   a. are another type of routine letter using the direct order.
   b. let people know the status of their orders.
   c. often follow form-letter format.
   d. can be used to welcome a new customer.
   e. all of the above.

8. A good opening for an acknowledgment letter to a new customer might be:
   a. Welcome as a buyer of Sinbad cosmetics!
   b. Your September 12 order for $765 worth of Sinbad cosmetics has been received.
   c. We are delighted to receive your order for Sinbad cosmetics.
   d. The Sinbad cosmetics you ordered September 12 were shipped today by Speedy Express Freight Lines and should reach you by Tuesday.
   e. Your September 12 order for Sinbad cosmetics makes us very happy.

9. When your company can't fill all of an order immediately, the acknowledgment letter should:
   a. emphasize what the company can and is doing to fill the order.
   b. let the reader know the bad news right away.
   c. use the indirect approach.
   d. remind the customer it is his or her fault for not giving complete information.
   e. apologize at length, particularly with a new customer.

10. In writing a personnel evaluation letter, you need to:
    a. distinguish between facts and opinions.
    b. remember that even reporting only verifiable facts can be unfair.
    c. be careful in handling negative points.
    d. try to communicate a true picture of the applicant.
    e. all of the above.

11. An adjustment-grant letter:
    a. is a good-news letter lending itself to direct treatment.
    b. must overcome a negative customer experience.
    c. needs to regain lost confidence in the company's product or service.
    d. needs to avoid use of negative words that recall the unpleasant situation the reader wrote about.
    e. all of the above.

12. Granting the customer's claim in an adjustment letter:
    a. requires an indirect approach because of the negative experience.
    b. will regain lost confidence in the company's product or service.
    c. should be accompanied by an apologetic explanation.
    d. should be accompanied by information that regains lost confidence.
    e. requires a complete apology in the last paragraph.

13. In best letter strategy, the last paragraph of a routine response:
    a. is adapted to the one case.
    b. includes sales talk.
    c. apologizes for problems the reader had.
    d. answers a major question.
    e. refers to the letter being answered.

14. An *ineffective* way to begin a direct letter is with:
    a. a reference to the date of the reader's letter in the first five words of the text.
    b. good news in the first paragraph.
    c. an explanation in the first paragraph.
    d. emphasis on the reader's self-interest in the first paragraph.
    e. a statement giving what the reader wants.

15. Direct organization of a letter:
    a. is appropriate only when the news is all good for the reader.
    b. requires that you get to the goal of the letter right away.
    c. needs a subject line to identify the situation.
    d. is appropriate for all replies to inquiries.
    e. starts with a general goodwill statement.

Completion

1. The primary goal of a letter in which you are able to answer an inquiry favorably is _____ _____.

2. Because you are able to give the customer what he/she wants, your good-news letter should follow the _____ order.

3. A mechanical device that helps to quickly identify the letter being answered is the _____ _____.

4. If you refer to the letter being answered in the text of your reply letter, you should do so _____ _____ rather than in a position of strong emphasis.

5. Bad news should be put in a position of _____ emphasis.

6. To avoid the appearance of giving hurried, routine answers and to achieve maximum goodwill results, you should include along with your answers _____ which show an interest in your reader's problem.

7. The primary goal of an individually written acknowledgment letter is to_____.

8. A second goal of individually written acknowledgment letters is to _____.

9. An acknowledgment letter should contain: first, _____, also _____, also _____, and, in close, _____.

10. The close of an individually written acknowledgment letter should (a) _____ and (b) _____.

11. A personnel evaluation calls for _____ order because you _____ _____.

12. Two ways of beginning a routine direct-order letter are by (a) _____ and (b) _____.

13. Identification of the letter to which you are responding should be done (where) _____ either by or _____.

14. Analysis of the job situation indicated in the reader's inquiry should guide your answer in a(n) _____ _____ letter situation.

15. Facts are preferred in a personnel evaluation, but if you are asked for an opinion you need to _____ _____ and _____.

16. In all letter situations you should try to make your words fit _____ for maximum goodwill results.

Application Exercises
Exercise 1:

Match with numbered positions in preceding diagram:

1. In a *routine reply letter*, identify position by filling in the appropriate number:
   _____ a. cordial words adapted to the one situation
   _____ b. mechanical device to identify letter being emphasized
   _____ c. numbered list of answers
   _____ d. statement indicating you are giving what the reader wants

2. What is the position of greatest emphasis? _____.

3. In the *acknowledgment letter*, identify position by filling in the appropriate number:
   _____ a. has a friendly, forward look and expresses appreciation for order
   _____ b. indicates when order will be shipped
   _____ c. talks about new products and services

4. In a *personnel-evaluation letter*, identify position by filling in the appropriate number:
   _____ a. mechanical device to identify letter being emphasized
   _____ b. expression of natural friendliness
   _____ c. systematic presentation of information
   _____ d. direct report of a significant fact

5. In an *adjustment-grant letter*, identify position by filling in the appropriate number:
   _____ a. regain lost confidence
   _____ b. identify situation to which you are responding
   _____ c. away from situation–toward future look at happy relations
   _____ d. direct statement of answer

Exercise 2:

As adjustment manager for the Pecos Valley Candy Company, Pine City, TX, you received the following letter from Ms. Robin Wyndell, owner of the Sweet Tooth Shoppe, 987 Lee Avenue, Atlanta, GA 30302.

> Dear Sir:
>
> Please send me my money back for that last shipment of Cashmere Candy Treats (eight dozen 1-pound boxes at $24.15 per dozen). The pecans in the candy are rancid. We have sold five boxes, and already three have been returned. We are losing money and customers. Also, tell me whether you want me to return the rancid candy back to you or to destroy them. Please let me hear from you soon.
>
> > Sincerely yours,

You find it difficult to believe that Ms. Wyndell's story is true, but your investigation proves that it is. Your system of dating all candies to be sure that fresh candy reaches your customers is still a good one. But it works only when you have honest people enforcing it. It seems that one of your stock people substituted some old candy, scheduled to be destroyed, for fresh candy. This employee then stole the fresh candy and sold it to a local gift-shop manager.

Of course, you'll give Ms. Wyndell her money back plus shipping costs. You will also try to explain the situation in order to keep her as a customer and to regain her confidence in your product and your company.

1. In this adjustment-grant letter, a good opening would be:
    a. Of course, you have the right to be upset about the rancid candies you received in your October 1st order.
    b. The enclosed check for $193.20 is Pecos Valley's way of showing you how highly we value your satisfaction.
    c. We have received your October 10th letter claiming that the 8 dozen boxes of Cashmere Candy Treats you got on October 5 were rancid.
    d. It's hard to believe that our system of dating candies to assure our customers of receiving only the freshest candies fouled us–and you!
    e. We want your customers to be satisfied with Cashmere Candy Treats, too.

2. A good explanation paragraph might begin:
    a. Unfortunately, our system of dating candies to insure our customers receive only fresh candy was sabotaged by a dishonest employee.
    b. Regretfully, we have to report the rancid candies were substituted for the candies you ordered by an employee who was selling the fresh candies on the side.
    c. We have fired the employee who sent you the wrong candies.
    d. Because we value your satisfaction, we investigated the reason you received the rancid candy your customers returned.
    e. After receiving your October 10 letter, we investigated the situation carefully.

3. The best close for this letter would be:
   a. Again let us apologize for the inconvenience you and your customers experienced.
   b. Give us another chance, and we promise you'll never be disappointed by rancid Cashmere Candy Treats again.
   c. We trust the preceding explanation has convinced you of our sincere concern for your customers' satisfaction.
   d. If we can be of further service, please let us know.
   e. The enclosed brochure illustrates our specially decorated keepsake tins filled with Christmas candies to delight your customers during the holiday season ahead.

4. Indicate the proper sequence for the following topics in constructing a reply to Ms. Wyndell; if not appropriate, indicate "NA":
   NA a. apology for inconvenience to customer
   NA b. subject line identifying situation
   2 c. explanation of exception to regular dating and inspection system
   3 d. instructions for disposing of rancid candy
   1 e. grant of customer request
   NA f. resale of company's products
   4 g. comments on a forthcoming sale

5. Identify the letter's objectives: a. *Regain loss confidence.*
                                      b. *Maintain goodwill*.

6. Identify the customer's likely reaction to the goals:

   Reluctant to order order again, but will.
   Be delighted with our cooperation.

7. Using the information on the previous page as a guide, write an adjustment letter to Ms. Wyndell.

Indirectness for Bad News

7

Multiple Choice (Circle the best answer)

1. To keep goodwill in a bad-news message, you should:
   a. identify the situation promptly.
   b. use a direct approach.
   c. include an explanation after giving the bad news.
   d. include an explanation before giving the bad news.
   e. put the bad news in an emphasis position.

2. Indirectness usually is good for:
   a. bad-news letters.
   b. adjustment grants and persuasive letters.
   c. adjustment grants and bad-news situations.
   d. claim letters and other bad-news situations.
   e. all routine correspondence.

3. Since a major goal of a refusal letter is to say no, you should:
   a. say no—plainly and directly.
   b. explain and justify your decision before refusing.
   c. apologize for the bad news.
   d. handle it as a routine message.
   e. tell the reader what he or she wants is against a company policy.

4. The opening paragraph in a bad-news letter should:
   a. identify the request to which you are responding.
   b. set up the strategy for moving into the explanation.
   c. avoid giving either a yes or no answer.
   d. be neutral.
   e. all of the above.

5. In getting the reader to accept your reasoning as fair and reasonable, you should:
   a. avoid negative words.
   b. use the you-viewpoint.
   c. emphasize the positive parts of the message.
   d. avoid emphasizing negative parts of the message.
   e. all of the above.

6. The most negative part of a refusal letter is:
   a. an alternative suggestion.
   b. the identification of the situation.
   c. the explanation of company policy.
   d. a review of supporting facts.
   e. the refusal.

7. When possible, it is good refusal strategy to:
   a. refuse in a position of emphasis.
   b. be definite by use of words such as no, not, cannot, and refuse.
   c. show regret or apologize.
   d. tell what you can do.
   e. be deliberately vague.

8. The reader demands your firm replace a faulty calculator, but your examination of the calculator convinces you it is not working because of harsh treatment after it was purchased. A good refusal in your bad-news letter might be:
   a. Our company policy prohibits replacement of calculators that have been abused by purchasers.
   b. The best we can do is repair your calculator for $15.
   c. If you had not abused the calculator, we could have considered replacing it.
   d. We regret that company policy won't let us do as you request.
   e. We cannot replace merchandise damaged after it is bought.

9. The close of a refusal letter should:
   a. repeat a major point of explanation.
   b. apologize for the refusal.
   c. ask for understanding by the reader.
   d. move to a friendly, off-subject topic.
   e. all are important.

10. The close in a refusal letter should:
    a. try to overcome the negative mood the reader may have after the refusal.
    b. depend on the facts of the specific case.
    c. avoid reference to the bad news.
    d. aim at creating a goodwill effect.
    e. all are important.

11. In developing the facts of the case for an adjustment refusal, you need to:
    a. try to mentally place yourself in the reader's position.
    b. question the reader's honesty.
    c. write from the company's point of view.
    d. remind the reader of facts she or he "forgot" or should know.
    e. emphasize the negative situation by using negative words.

12. A tactful credit-refusal letter will:
    a. begin indirectly.
    b. refuse clearly.
    c. work to build goodwill.
    d. try to cultivate cash sales.
    e. all of the above.

Completion

1. When telling bad news in a letter, you can soften the harshness and help maintain goodwill by giving a(n) _____ before you give the bad news.

2. Three bad-news letter situations that usually use the indirect approach rather than the direct are (a) _____ _____, (b) _____, and (c) _____.

3. The two goals of a refusal letter are to (a) _____, and (b) _____.

4. In order to satisfy the second goal, you need to _____ and _____ your decision so as to convince the reader that "no" is fair and reasonable.

5. In a bad-news letter, beginning directly would likely put the reader in a(n) _____ frame of mind to read the explanation.

6. In developing a fair explanation for a refusal, you should do three things before you begin to write—they are (a) _____, (b) _____, and (c) _____.

7. The opening in a refusal letter should accomplish three things: (a) _____, (b) _____, and (c) _____.

8. A convincing presentation of your explanation should lead the reader to accept the refusal as a(n) _____ _____.

9. To avoid emphasizing the refusal, you should say it
   1) quickly —(explain) _____.
   2) clearly — (explain)_____.
   3) positively —(explain) _____.

10. The close of a refusal should be friendly and off-subject in order to serve the _____ goal.

11. The explanation that justifies the refusal should be written with the _____ viewpoint in mind.

12. Two good reasons for being tactful and considerate in writing a credit refusal are (a) _____ _____ and (b) _____.

Application Exercises
Exercise 1:

1. Each major letter type has a certain "flow" or sequence of action. From the list below, select "building blocks" and list them in the sequence you would use for the refusal letter plan. Some, but not all, of the items may be used.

   a. set up strategy
   b. gain attention
   c. justify reasoning
   d. identify situation to which responding
   e. present explanation
   f. use neutral approach
   g. state refusal positively
   h. make request
   i. suggest action wanted.
   j. make off-subject, friendly comment.
   k. suggest benefit to reader

   opening (1) _____
   middle (2) _____
   close (3) _____

2. Of the following letter types we have studied so far, identify which usually need the direct (D) and which the indirect (I) letter strategy.

_____	claim letter	_____	routine response
_____	adjustment grant	_____	request refusal
_____	adjustment refusal	_____	order letter
_____	routine inquiry	_____	personnel evaluation
_____	credit refusal		

Exercise 2:

In the role of public relations director for Thor Products Manufacturing Company, you must answer a letter written by Mr. Pat Morris, a fourth-grade teacher from an elementary school in a nearby suburb. Mr. Morris has asked to bring his class of 30 students to visit your factory next Friday. He is certain the Thor Products people won't mind, and he'll have a couple of mothers along to keep the kids in line.

Because of potential dangers throughout the plant, Thor Products management doesn't even allow adult groups to visit the production areas. There are just too many things that could go wrong. You know it will be a disappointment to the kids, for Mr. Morris's letter tells how excited they are about the visit. As a compromise, you would be willing to visit his class and show a film on your operation. You also would bring along some sample products as gifts for the kids.

A possible reply:

Dear Mr. Morris:

Unfortunately, potential dangers throughout the plant make it impossible for us to grant your request to bring your fourth-grade class to Thor Products. Even with the mothers to help chaperon the kids, there is too much that could go wrong. We don't even allow adult groups to visit the production area.

We do have a film that shows our operation, and I would be glad to show it to your class myself. I could also bring some sample products for the kids so they won't be too disappointed.

This could save you and the mothers a lot of trouble besides. I am pretty busy, but if you will call my secretary, we ought to be able to get together on a time fairly soon. Sorry we couldn't grant your request, but I'm sure you'll appreciate our concern for the kids' safety.

Yours truly,

1. Identify some of the major problems in the preceding reply:

Threat ~~Threat~~

Direct beginning

Too many negative words.

Close ~~reminds~~ of the ~~fact~~ rejection

~~Not~~ Not a good close; should be ~~so~~ more ~~businesslike~~

2. Arrange the following topics to form an outline for another letter you could write in this case:
   - _1_ a. expression of pleasure that students are interested in Thor Products
   - _3_ b. offer to visit the class
   - _5_ c. your telephone number where teacher can confirm convenient time for visit—which you look forward to
   - _2_ d. explanation of safety measures Thor Products follows to protect employees and visitors of all ages
   - _4_ e. comment on interesting feature of the film and gifts

3. A good opening sentence for your letter might be:
   a. Because of potential dangers throughout the plant, Thor Products has a restrictive visitors policy.
   b. We regret that potential dangers throughout the plant create an unsafe situation for visitors of all ages.
   c. We were delighted to hear of the interest your fourth-graders have in learning about Thor Products.
   d. It hurts us that we must disappoint your fine class of fourth-graders, but our plant simply is too dangerous for children.
   e. In reply to your letter of October 17th, let me explain our firm's visitors policy.

4. A good transition to the following explanation might be:
   a. Because of potential dangers throughout the plant, Thor Products has a restrictive visitors policy that applies to all ages.
   b. We welcome the opportunity to do all we can to help tomorrow's adults become better acquainted with modern manufacturing processes.
   c. Because of safety rules in effect at the plant, we'd like to suggest a compromise.
   d. However, as you know, what we'd like to do isn't always possible.
   e. However, we'd like to suggest that you let us bring Thor Products to your classroom instead.

5. Now you've started. Write you complete reply in the space below:

Indirectness in Persuasion and Sales Writing

8

Multiple Choice (Circle the best answer)

1. The opening of a persuasive letter differs from that of a refusal in that it:
    a. begins directly.
    b. starts with a request.
    c. expresses the writer's pleasure.
    d. sets up the strategy for following persuasion.
    e. introduces the writer.

2. In a persuasive letter, the request itself:
    a. should follow convincing explanation.
    b. should be preceded by a logical and orderly presentation of reasoning.
    c. requires care in word choice.
    d. can end the letter.
    e. all of the above.

3. Indirect-order strategy is appropriate for:
    a. claims and adjustment grants.
    b. credit refusals and persuasive requests.
    c. persuasive requests and routine inquiries.
    d. sales and credit inquiries.
    e. personnel evaluations and persuasive requests.

4. Something you need to study before beginning to write a sales letter is:
    a. what the product will do.
    b. exactly what is included in the service.
    c. the customers' economic status and education.
    d. the customers' age and culture.
    e. all of the above.

5. An example of an emotional appeal would be:
    a. saving time and money.
    b. having greater durability.
    c. saving energy costs.
    d. being more attractive to the opposite sex.
    e. all of the above.

6. An example of a rational appeal would be:
    a. safety features and better gas mileage in a car.
    b. a "whiter, brighter" smile from a toothpaste.
    c. "the new you" promised by a new perfume or cologne.
    d. the higher status suggested by a mink coat.
    e. all of the above.

7. The type of appeal(s) you decide on using in a sales letter depend on:
    a. what the nature of the product or service is.
    b. which appeals best fit the customers.
    c. whether you are selling for resale or final use.
    d. what purpose the product will be used for.
    e. all of the above.

8. One of the best attention-getting devices in a sales letter is a:
    a. statement introducing a need the product will satisfy.
    b. "Dear Occupant" or "Dear Resident" greeting.
    c. sensational claim for the product.
    d. strong closing drive for action.
    e. you-viewpoint adaptation.

9. Sales-message writing:
    a. follows other direct writing patterns.
    b. always follows the indirect approach.
    c. can be quite different from normal business writing.
    d. avoids folksy writing and one-sentence paragraphs.
    e. seldom uses mechanical devices for emphasis.

10. Probably the most important pronoun you can use in a sales letter is:
    a. I.
    b. we.
    c. they.
    d. you.
    e. it.

11. The information you include in a sales letter should:
    a. leave none of the reader's questions unanswered.
    b. not fail to overcome any objections the reader might have.
    c. include all basic points.
    d. be clear and convincing.
    e. all of the above.

12. A good way to supplement the main sales message in the sales letter is to:
    a. use enclosures.
    b. use mechanical devices for emphasis.
    c. use diagrams and pictures.
    d. use color and headlines.
    e. write a long (i.e., 4-page) letter after the salutation.

13. The close in a sales letter:
    a. needs to be off-subject.
    b. needs to urge action.
    c. thanks the reader for taking the time to read the letter.
    d. asks the reader to read the enclosure(s).
    e. all of the above.

14. Letters can be written to sell:
    a. products and services.
    b. ideas.
    c. the company.
    d. yourself.
    e. all of the above.

15. Attention-getting techniques in sales letters:
    a. are unnecessary, as the customer wants to hear about the product.
    b. may be either short or long.
    c. are effective only for the final users of a product.
    d. require use of gimmicks.
    e. must tell a story.

16. The drive for action in the close of a sales letter:
    a. should take the reader through the steps of what he or she must do.
    b. should only hint at the desired action.
    c. should never be followed by a postscript.
    d. must not use hard-sell tactics by urging immediacy.
    e. is unnecessary if the rest of the letter is well written.

17. Selling to a dealer:
    a. typically uses a rational approach.
    b. typically uses an emotional approach.
    c. does not use the you-viewpoint as much as selling to a final user.
    d. means emphasizing final user benefits.
    e. depends on offering a free gift or discount price.

18. Strength can be added to a sales effort by:
    a. using attention-gaining mechanical techniques.
    b. emphasizing the you-viewpoint thought.
    c. using a postscript.
    d. using a second, follow-up letter.
    e. all of the above have been used effectively.

Completion

1. Although it is not a bad-news letter, a persuasive request also requires using the _____ letter order.

2. Try to anticipate the reader's _____ in deciding what will be a convincing explanation in the persuasive letter.

3. In addition to setting up the strategy in a persuasive-request letter, you will need to use the opening to _____.

4. Before you start to write a sales letter, you need to know about the _____ or _____ and about _____ as well.

5. Depending on the product, some appeals you might decide to use in writing a sales letter include (a) _____, (b) _____, (c) _____, and (d) _____.

6. Two major categories of appeals are _____ and _____.

7. If you are selling fancy candies, you might use the _____ appeal to reach the final user but use the _____ appeal if you were selling to a retailer.

8. The first requirement of the opening in a sales letter is to _____.

9. Factual material is apt to follow a(n) _____ appeal in a sales letter, while selling the product in terms of its effects on the reader's senses follows a(n) _____ appeal.

10. People are persuaded best through an appeal to _____ self-interest.

11. Be sure to give enough information so that none of the questions a reader might have are _____ _____.

12. Enclosures should be used in sales letters only to _____ the main message.

13. The close in a sales letter should _____ and/or _____.

14. Most sales letters are written by _____.

15. Practice in writing sales letters helps each person by teaching _____.

16. A currently popular technique in writing sales letters uses the strategy of communicating quickly by placing a(n) _____ at the beginning.

17. In a sales package using a letter and several enclosures, it is important that all pieces should present a(n) _____ message.

Application Exercises
Exercise 1:

1. Each major letter type has a certain "flow" or sequence of action. From the list below, select "building blocks" and list them in the sequence you would use for the persuasion letter plan. Some, but not all, of the items may be used.

   a. set up strategy
   b. gain attention
   c. justify reasoning
   d. identify situation to which responding
   e. present explanation
   f. use neutral approach
   g. state refusal positively
   h. make request
   i. suggest action wanted
   j. make off-subject, friendly comment.
   k. suggest benefit to reader

   opening   _____
   middle   _____
   close   _____

Exercise 2:

1. Arrange the following in the proper sequence for developing a good sales letter:
   _____ a. recall a reader benefit
   _____ b. urge action
   _____ c. gain attention
   _____ d. show how product satisfies need
   _____ e. identify reader need
   _____ f. set up strategy

2. Identify the following appeals as rational (R) or emotional (E).

_____ long lasting, durable finish
_____ the plush feel of a fur coat
_____ energy-saving features
_____ economical to use
_____ taste-tingling soft drink
_____ hickory-smoked fragrance of bacon
_____ buy American-made products
_____ saving money through purchasing now
_____ making a profit on reselling product
_____ security device for peace-of-mind

Exercise 3:

Your business, Tri-Star Bakeries, Inc., 1417 Rocky-Mountain Avenue, Boulder, Colorado, has built its reputation over the years by catering to parties and providing exclusive bakery products for weddings, anniversaries, birthdays, and the like. Today, you have a new idea that should increase sales and profits.

Since your pastry products have always been considered excellent and because of your close proximity to the University of Colorado campus, you are determined to tap a new market, that of college first-year students. Parents of that group, you reason, would certainly like the idea of remembering their children on their birthdays—particularly the first year away from home. All you need, you decide, is a direct-mail letter to convince the parents that they should buy birthday cakes and have them delivered to the students personally on their birthdays.

1. Identify your market._____
_____

2. What benefit can you offer people? _____
_____
_____
_____
_____
_____

3. What buying motive would the cake appeal to? _____
_____
_____

4. Will your best approach be an emotional or a rational appeal? _____
_____
_____
_____

5. Write the letter. This will be a form letter, but each will be individually processed. Assume you are including an enclosure giving descriptions, flavors, sizes, and prices. You will also include a postcard for easy return. (*Hint:* First review the checkpoint list for sales letters below. Then write. After you finish, compare your letter to the checkpoints to see if your letter covers the requirements.)

Checkpoints for sales letters:

A — I — D — A formula

In the OPENING, did you:
1) get *attention*?
2) set up selling strategy?
3) put reader self-interest in the first sentence?

In developing your sales message, did you:
4) arouse *interest*?
5) stress the you-viewpoint? reader benefits?
6) develop selling strategy?
7) overcome possible objections?
8) include all necessary information?
9) create *desire* for product?

In the CLOSE, did you:
10) seek *action*?
11) take reader through motions of whatever is necessary to complete transaction? (make it sound easy)
12) stress immediacy in action?
13) recall a major reader benefit?

Somewhere in the letter, did you:
14) use the student's name?

Memorandums

9

Multiple Choice (Circle the best answer)

1. Memorandums may be classified into two types:
    a. those like letters, those like proposals.
    b. those like proposals, those like reports.
    c. those like letters, those like reports.
    d. those like informal notes, those like letters.

2. Mark the main heading (or headings) that is appropriate for memorandum stationery.
    a. Memorandum
    b. Interoffice Correspondence
    c. Office Memo
    d. All of the above.

3. Mark the appropriate order (or orders) of headings for memorandums:
    a. Date, To, From, Subject
    b. To, From, Subject, Date
    c. Date, From, To, Subject
    d. All are appropriate.

4. When printed memorandum stationery is not available, the heading information may be typed along with the message using this arrangement:
    a. To, From, Subject, Date
    b. Date, To, From, Subject
    c. Date, Plant Location, Department, To, From, Subject
    d. Any of the above are appropriate.

5. Electronic memos differ from printed memos in that:
    a. they have need to be organized so that their contents are in "chunks."
    b. they have a greater need to let the reader know their contents early.
    c. they have a greater need for subheads.
    d. all of the above.

6. Minimum length for a memorandum is:
    a. one line.
    b. two lines.
    c. five lines.
    d. ten lines.

7. The most common forms of memorandums are:
    a. routine inquiries and persuasive requests.
    b. routine presentations of information and bad-news messages.
    c. routine inquiries and routine presentations of information.
    d. persuasive requests and bad-news messages.

8. A memorandum written by a department head to the board of directors most likely would be written:
   a. in personal style (I, we, you, etc.).
   b. in impersonal style (third person).
   c. as an informal note.
   d. as a persuasive request.

9. Memorandums carrying negative news:
   a. always should be written in indirect order.
   b. always should be written in direct order.
   c. should be written indirectly when the bad news is of major personal concern to the reader.
   d. should be written indirectly when the reader is a subordinate of the writer.

10. As memorandum writers usually have little need to be concerned about the effect of their words, they should:
    a. be unconcerned about harshness and unfriendliness.
    b. practice the courtesy friendly people use when working together.
    c. always use the indirect order.
    d. write in the third person.

11. Which of the following is *not* characteristic of the most typical memorandums?
    a. You-viewpoint language
    b. Conversational language
    c. Clear language
    d. Directness

Completion

1. Memorandums are defined as _____ written inside the organization.

2. Typically, rather than sign the memorandum, the writer _____ it.

3. In place of preprinted stationary many companies use _____ for making meno headings.

4. Although memorandums vary somewhat in the degree of their formality, they tend to be _____
   _____.

5. The more formal reports are written in the _____ person and the more informal ones in the _____ person.

6. The principles for writing memorandums are much the same as for writing _____.

7. Although letters and memorandums are much alike, they are different in two major ways:
   (1) _____, and
   (2) _____
   _____.

8. Instead of emphasizing the effect of words on readers, the memorandum writer's primary concern is for _____
   _____
   _____.

9. A memorandum making a routine request for information should begin _____.

10. A memorandum carrying bad news should begin indirectly when _____
    _____.

11. Although they are rare, memorandums persuasively requesting something are appropriately written in the
_____ order.

12. A memorandum that records an event or activity that its writer wants to make a record of for future reference
is called _____.

Application Exercises

Assume that you are the vice president for promotion for Penwick's, Inc., a chain of 47 stores selling men's quality
clothing. Your office prepares all major promotions for all stores, including the layout and copy for newspaper
advertising. At the moment your staff has just completed newspaper advertisements for your annual week-long Easter
sale. It features a selection of quality spring fashions—including DeVillier dress suits, Lark custom shirts, Valle ties,
and Peyton shoes. As a special attraction the ad includes a coupon good for a 10 percent discount on all sale items
purchased during the sale.

Although it is a few weeks before the sale, you will write a memorandum informing all store managers of what you
have done. In addition, you will instruct them to keep detailed records of this promotion so that you can evaluate its
results. Specifically, you'll want the dollar sales of each advertised item, as well as the store's total sales for the
period. Also, you'll want the number of customers taking advantage of the discount coupon and the dollar amount
of the discounts given. This information, you feel, will give you some measure of the success of the promotion.

1. In addition to the conventional Date, To, From, Subject headings, Pinwick's printed memorandum stationery
is likely to have headings for _Department, Store, At_____
_____.

2. Even though the message of this memorandum will mean hard work for the readers and thus may be considered
bad news, you will write it in the direct order. Also, you will not need to be concerned about the effect of your
words (no need for you-viewpoint, positive emphasis, or such). You can write this memorandum this way
because:
internal written messages giving work rules
procedures instructions & the like are common in
most large organizations.
_____
_____

3. The identification information for the subject line of this memorandum probably would include two items:
(1) _Upcoming annual Easter Sale_____,
_____ and
(2) _Sale items (Preparations for the Sale)_____
_10% discount_____.

4. A good beginning sentence for this memorandum would cover _the newspaper advertisement_

5. The remainder of the memorandum probably would include:
The quality spring fashions advertised in newspaper.
10% discount on all the sale items purchased.
Instructions given in order to evaluate the result
of the sale.

6. In the space below, write the memorandum that follows the plan described on the previous page.

Pattern Variations in Collections

10

Multiple Choice (Circle the best answer)

1. Most collection letter attempts:
   a. are the same for all classes of customers.
   b. are the same for all fields of business.
   c. are the same for individuals and businesses.
   d. move through a series of mild-to-strong efforts.
   e. all of the above.

2. The sequence in the collection procedure:
   a. moves directly and swiftly.
   b. moves indirectly and slowly.
   c. assumes first the customer *will* pay, second the customer *should* pay, and last the customer *must* pay.
   d. is never concerned with goodwill, as the customer has already shown bad faith.
   e. is appropriate only for cases that can be handled on an individual basis.

3. A slower moving first-stage series of letters is apt to be written before moving to the second stage in the case of:
   a. customers who are usually good credit risks.
   b. customers who are poor credit risks.
   c. customers with budget accounts.
   d. other business.
   e. all should be treated the same.

4. The typical first collection letter:
   a. is short.
   b. is written in direct order.
   c. assumes the customer will pay.
   d. may include goodwill talk.
   e. all of the above.

5. The middle-stage collection letter:
   a. is indirect.
   b. develops a basic reader self-interest appeal.
   c. uses persuasive strategy.
   d. tries to convince the customer that he/she *should* pay.
   e. all of the above.

6. The beginning of a middle-stage collection letter:
   a. requests payment immediately.
   b. strives to gain reader attention immediately, similar to sales letter opening strategy.
   c. uses a buffer/neutral opening, similar to a refusal letter.
   d. uses a direct approach, similar to a routine request.
   e. none of the above.

7. To be truly effective, a persuasive collection appeal:
   a. should be introduced in the second paragraph.
   b. should be introduced in the second paragraph and repeated in the close.
   c. should be presented in terms of the reader's self-interest.
   d. must emphasize the collector's patience.
   e. b, c, and d.

8. Lecturing the reader forcefully about his or her negligence in paying a bill is apt to:
   a. arouse antagonism and resistance.
   b. build goodwill.
   c. convince the reader you are really serious about collecting.
   d. convince the reader you are friendly yet firm.
   e. result in keeping the reader as a good customer later on.

9. In the close of a middle-stage collection letter, it is permissible to:
   a. ask for payment.
   b. refer to the reader's past-due account.
   c. make the desired action sound easy to take.
   d. refer to a benefit the reader receives by paying.
   e. all of the above.

10. A good first sentence for a first-stage collection letter might be:
    a. What shall we report about you?
    b. I am very much disappointed that you ignored our last reminder that your account is past due in the amount of $99.
    c. You have not responded to the past two statements we sent you and are now two months past due on your account.
    d. Won't you take a moment to write a check for the $97.20 now two months past due on your account?
    e. How would you write a good friend on an embarrassing subject?

11. You have moved to the middle stage. A good opening sentence early in the series would be:
    a. What shall we report about you?
    b. I am very much disappointed that you ignored our last reminder that your account is past due in the amount of $99.
    c. You have not responded to the past two statements we sent you and are now two months past due on your account.
    d. Won't you take a moment to write a check for the $97.20 now two months past due on your account?
    e. How would you write a good friend on an embarrassing subject?

12. You are still writing, but you are ready to make this the last of your middle-stage appeals. A good way to start this letter is:
    a. What shall we report about you?
    b. I am very much disappointed that you ignored our last reminder that your account is past due in the amount of $99.
    c. You have not responded to the past two statements we sent you and are now two months past due on your account.
    d. Won't you take a moment to write a check for the $97.20 now two months past due on your account?
    e. How would you write a good friend on an embarrassing subject?

13. In the last-resort collection letter, it is appropriate for you to:
    a. use a direct approach.
    b. point out the disadvantages of not paying to the reader.
    c. state what you are going to do to collect.
    d. state a final deadline.
    e. all of the above.

14. In the last-resort collection letter, you:
    a. are emphasizing goodwill.
    b. need to maintain a firm and considerate—not angry—tone.
    c. use a neutral opening.
    d. use only positive appeals.
    e. all of the above.

Completion

1. The most common method of trying to collect on past-due bills is by _____.

2. In a three-stage collection effort, the writer assumes in the first stage that the customer _____ pay, in the second stage that the customer _____, and in the third and final stage that the customer_____.

3. The number of letters and the length of time a company takes to move through the three stages usually depends on (a) _____ and (b) _____.

4. Both direct and indirect styles are used in the series. Usually the first, early-stage letters use the _____ _____ style.

5. Middle-stage letters in the collection series use the _____ style.

6. The final, last-resort letter uses the _____ style.

7. One or more reminders written in a friendly tone are typical of the _____ stage of collection letters.

8. Use of persuasion is typical of the _____ stage.

9. Examples of persuasive appeals are (a) _____ (b) _____, and (c) _____.

10. You want to avoid insulting or otherwise making the reader angry in the middle stage because your goal still is to _____ and an angry reader is more apt to _____.

11. While remaining friendly and positive in tone, it is logical to make each additional middle-stage letter _____.

12. As an example, earlier letters in the middle stage emphasize _____ of paying, while the last one(s) may point out the _____ paying.

13. An early middle-stage appeal might be _____, while a stronger late appeal is _____.

14. Direct style in the last-resort stage means beginning the letter _____ _____.

15. Writing to the reader's viewpoint in a last-resort letter means using persuasive appeals such as _____ and _____.

Application Exercises

Exercise 1:

You are the advertising sales manager for the Miami Dolphins professional football team. Early last summer you sold a four-color, inside cover page of the Dolphins' program for all eight home games to Mr. Alonzo "Rib" Bruiser. "Rib," a former Baltimore Colts player now retired, operates Rib's Rib House, a fancy restaurant in nearby Hialeah.

"Rib" paid you $2,000 when he bought the ad space, and he agreed to pay the balance of $6,000 within four weeks. You billed him shortly before the due date. Two weeks later you billed him again. After waiting two more weeks, you wrote a reminder letter in which you were tactful but indicated you expected to get the money to help pay for the 150,000 programs already printed.

He still didn't respond. So now you'll have to write another letter. This one, which will be mailed a full month after the reminder letter, will contain an attempt to persuade the big man to pay.

As you think through the letter, you look for an appeal that will fit this big, retired football player. You decide on a fair-play theme. As you see it, one accustomed to teamwork and to competitive sports certainly should have a keen appreciation of fair play. But you will need to be cautious so that you do not offend this man.

The letter you write will be an early middle-stage collection letter. Review middle-stage letter strategy. Now complete the following questions and write the letter.

1. Middle-stage strategy uses the (direct/indirect) approach. This means you will need to start by _____ _____ and setting up strategy in your opening paragraph.

2. In the second paragraph you will develop your _____ appeal. Remember to adapt to the _____ point of view. You will be persuasive but tactful.

3. In the close you will ask _____ directly; and to strengthen the request you will refer to a _____ to "Rib" in paying promptly.

Exercise 2:

Unfortunately, Mr. Bruiser did not reply to the letter you wrote in Exercise 1 or another letter featuring an appeal to pride or a third appealing to self-interest. You must write a last-resort letter today. Review last-resort letter strategy.

1. The letter you write will use direct/indirect strategy. In the beginning paragraph you will indicate clearly ____ _____, with a subtle reference to information that justifies the action.

2. The second paragraph is still persuasive, still takes the you-viewpoint. You will select _____ _____ for an appeal and show "Rib" what your action will mean to him.

3. Your close will call for _____ by "Rib" with a specific deadline. Take time to remind him of what he can gain if he does.

4. Now write this letter that you hope will finally get you the money. Don't sound angry, but be firm. You still can't believe such forceful measures are necessary or that "Rib" wants you to have to use them.

Strategy in Job Search and Application

11

Multiple Choice (Circle the best answer)

1. For a recent college graduate seeking a first full-time job, part-time experience involving menial work:
   a. is of little or no importance.
   b. is more important than any other background information.
   c. can be presented effectively to show work ethic.
   d. is useful to demonstrate personality.
   e. can be used effectively to show professional competency.

2. Which of the following would *not* be part of the conventional organizational headings in a resume?
   a. Work Experiences
   b. Specialized Training in (your area of education)
   c. Personal Qualities
   d. Expected Salary and Promotions
   e. People Who Know My Abilities

3. Writing application letters is similar to writing
   a. routine inquiries.
   b. personnel inquiries.
   c. sales letters.
   d. acknowledgment letters.
   e. adjustment refusals.

4. The most important step in preparing to write an application letter is to
   a. become familiar with national and regional employment statistics.
   b. study carefully your product (you) and the prospective employer.
   c. review good interview procedures.
   d. read job listings in a newspaper.
   e. select references.

5. The resume should be used
   a. in place of an application letter.
   b. to provide significant details supporting the letter.
   c. at all times to add information to the letter.
   d. only when the employer asks for it.
   e. only if you have not personally met a company representative (i.e., interviewer).

6. Which of the following probably should *not* be included in the information on a resume?
   a. Dates, places and firms under work experience
   b. Duties and responsibilities under work experience
   c. Dates, institutions, degrees, and specialized areas of study under education
   d. Address (temporary and permanent) and phone number(s) under personal information
   e. Race, religion, and sex under personal information

7. In writing the resume you will need to
   a. use complete sentences.
   b. use personal pronouns.
   c. try to make all the information fit on one page.
   d. use the same grammatical form for equal-level captions.
   e. keep it as short as possible.

8. Under references you
   a. list a reference for every major job held recently.
   b. list people who can verify the points on which you base your appeal for the job.
   c. include accurate mailing addresses and appropriate job titles.
   d. offer an explanation if you do not include a reference.
   e. do all of the above.

9. The application letter:
   a. explains all the facts in the resume in greater detail.
   b. uses an indirect opening to be polite.
   c. fits the facts from your background to the work you are applying for.
   d. need not be concerned with the you-approach since you must say what "I can do" or "I have done."
   e. must cover details from all of the four major background areas discussed in the resume.

10. The approach you take in beginning your application letter:
    a. is limited only by your imagination.
    b. should take into consideration the nature of the job you seek.
    c. can tell the reader how much the company needs you.
    d. should not mention any in-company contacts you might possibly have.
    e. can be built on how much you need a job.

11. In the opening paragraph of an application letter, you need to
    a. use some positive techniques to gain reader interest.
    b. tell the reader when you will be able to start work.
    c. try to be amusing and/or "chummy."
    d. start with "I."
    e. rely on a safe-and-sure, old-style opening.

12. Before you decide what facts to present about yourself in the letter, you should:
    a. study the job to determine its requirements.
    b. try to learn something about the company.
    c. analyze your own strengths.
    d. a and b.
    e. a, b, and c.

13. As you look forward to graduation at the end of the semester, you are preparing a general-prospecting application letter. You decide the best organization plan for the letter would be:
    a. some logical grouping of information, such as education, personal details, and experience.
    b. a sequential plan showing step-by-step preparation for the work.
    c. an arrangement based on job requirements.
    d. a strict presentation of facts using the four most common background areas as separate, numbered paragraphs.
    e. any of the above that allows you to be the most imaginative in gaining attention.

14. In the close of your application letter, you might:
    a. ask for the job and tell the reader when you can start.
    b. ask for an interview or invite further correspondence.
    c. use a question to drive for action.
    d. recall a benefit the reader will receive from taking the action.
    e. b, c, and d.

15. You are answering an advertisement in the *Washington Post* for a personable individual with specialized training in accounting and who is willing to travel. You decide the best organization plan to use in writing an application letter for the job is
    a. some logical grouping of information, such as education, personal details, and experience.
    b. a sequential plan showing step-by-step preparation for the work.
    c. an arrangement based on job requirements.
    d. a strict presentation of facts using the four most common background areas as separate, numbered paragraphs.
    e. any of the above that allows you to be the most imaginative in gaining attention.

16. In the five years since you graduated and started as a management trainee with your present company, you have been given a variety of jobs, each with increasing levels of responsibility. While you like your job, the company is family-owned with two sons moving up the executive ladder. The father is president. You feel you have added valuable experience to your education over the years but want to join a larger company with better possibilities for advancement. A friend has told you of a position requiring experience such as you have gained, so you decide to write an application letter using as an organizational plan
    a. some logical grouping of information, such as education, personal details, and experience
    b. a sequential plan showing step-by-step preparation for the work
    c. an arrangement based on job requirements
    d. a strict presentation of facts using the four most common background areas as separate, numbered paragraphs
    e. any of the above that allows you to be the most imaginative in gaining attention

17. Which is the best of these suggestions for one being interviewed for a job?
    a. Show your strong personality by taking control of the interview.
    b. Ask a few questions—help control the dialogue.
    c. Let the interviewer control the interview completely.
    d. Give the interviewer a written list of questions you want to answer.
    e. Show respect by making answers as short as possible.

18. Your thank-you letter to the interviewer could contain
    a. additional information you forgot to mention in the interview.
    b. a hopeful look to the next step in the negotiations.
    c. additional information the interviewer requested (such as a completed application form).
    d. an expression of gratefulness.
    e. all of the above.

Completion

1. In building your network of contacts in the job search, the best way to get your professors to know you is by
_____
_____.

2. In analyzing yourself in the job search, you should review these categories of your qualifications:

   (1) _____

   (2) _____

   (3) _____

   (4) _____

3. In your search for an employer, you should consider these sources: (1) _____,

   (2) _____,

   (3) _____,

   (4) _____,

   (5) _____,"

   (6)_____.

4. The formal, organized arrangement of background information about yourself that outlines major details of your work experience and education is called the _____.

5. Resumes may be classified into two types: (a) the _____ type and (b) the _____ type.

6. The four most commonly used groupings of information on a resume are (a) _____,

   (b) _____,

   (c) _____,

   and (d) _____.

7. When you first graduate, your strongest selling point probably will be your _____, but as you gain experience you will give it _____ emphasis in the resume.

8. One absolutely essential bit of information you must include on your resume is _____.

9. In a sales letter you are trying to convince the readers a product or service meets a need. In an application letter you are trying to convince the reader that _____ meets the company needs.

10. To write the most effective application letter, you need to make a detailed inventory of _____ and a study of the _____.

11. In an application letter, as in a sales letter, you need to _____ the points you choose to emphasize to fit the _____.

12. Because the reader is likely to be busy, the opening of an application letter needs to (a) _____, and (b) _____.

13. When choosing what information to present about yourself, you should first review _____ _____.

14. In presenting the facts that fit you for the job, you can make your application letter even more effective by interpreting the information in terms of _____.

15. As in a sales letter, the close of an application letter should contain a drive for action. In an application letter this may consist of _____.

16. If you use both an application letter and resume, you should use the letter to _____ _____ and use the resume to _____.

17. Good advice concerning how to dress for a job interview is _____.

18. After an interview with an on-campus recruiter, writing a _____
    singles you out from the other interviewees and re-emphasizes your interest in the job.

19. Follow-up letters, whether about an interview or a job offer, or making an inquiry about the status of an earlier
    application letter, tend to share the following characteristics: _____
    and _____.

20. In addition, a follow-up to an application or a job acceptance would be written in the _____
    order, while a job-refusal letter would be written in the _____
    order.

Application Exercises

Part 1:   As a first step, you need to do some research. On the left-hand side of the page list your strengths—
do not underestimate yourself. On the right-hand side, analyze a job you would like or a job advertised in a newspaper (as your teacher prefers), and list what you believe the job requirements are.

My Strengths	*Job Requirements*

Part 2:   Go back to your analysis of your strengths and the job's requirements. From your list of strong points, select the ones that meet the needs of the company's job requirements. These are the points you will want to emphasize in your letter. List them below.

Part 3:   Follow the style of the general-purpose resume in the chapter and develop your own personal resume.

_____
(your name)

Employment Objective:

Education:

Experience:

Professional Skills:

Activities:

Interests:

References:

Telephone:

Address:

After completing Part 3, go back to Part 1 and see if you had forgotten any personal strengths the summary of details on your resume may have reminded you of. Add them.

Part 4:   Now write the application letter for the job you analyzed in Part 1. Remember the following check-points:

Opening: Gain attention.
           Set up the review of information that follows.

Content: Present information that qualifies you for the job.
           Present facts from background area (education, experience, personal qualities) and relate them to the job requirements. Develop only one major area per paragraph.
           Use one of three organizational plans suggested under the heading "Organizing for Conviction" in Chapter 11.
           Present facts in reader-viewpoint language as much as possible.

Close: Drive for appropriate action.
           Recall benefit reader will receive from taking the action.

Now write your letter, and then compare it again with the checklist. If you were a personnel director, would you ask the person who wrote this letter in for a job interview?

Basics of Report Writing

12

Multiple Choice (Circle the best answer)

1. Written reports are important to large organizations because they:
   a. make permanent records.
   b. can be routed to many readers easily.
   c. allow readers to review and study the result of investigations at their convenience.
   d. provide information that helps coordinate organizational work.
   e. all of the above.

2. All business reports must:
   a. cover human preferences and include conclusions.
   b. be factual and include recommendations.
   c. be orderly and serve a business purpose.
   d. be objective and communicate formally.
   e. cover only facts and never make interpretations.

3. In conducting your preliminary investigation into the report problem, it is appropriate to:
   a. check information already published on the subject.
   b. get the opinion of experts.
   c. discuss the problem with those authorizing it.
   d. search company files for relevant material.
   e. any or all of the above may be appropriate.

4. After you have investigated the problem situation, it is a good idea to develop a problem statement in writing because:
   a. it is then permanently preserved and other people can evaluate it.
   b. you may forget by Monday what you had decided the problem was on Friday.
   c. it forces you to think through the problem.
   d. you can show it to whoever authorized it so they can tell you if it is really what they had in mind.
   e. all of the above.

5. Which of the following is an example of a problem statement in infinitive phrase form?
   a. Personnel turnover is high, and management wants to know why.
   b. What are the causes of high personnel turnover?
   c. The causes of personnel turnover need to be investigated.
   d. To determine the causes of high personnel turnover.
   e. The investigation will look for the causes of high personnel turnover.

6. After getting the problem clearly in mind, next you will need to:
   a. decide what subject areas you need to investigate to study the problem.
   b. check the library for secondary sources.
   c. talk over the problem with experts.
   d. develop a detailed outline.
   e. take a break.

7. When you have collected the facts for your report, your next logical step is to:
   a. write the report.
   b. prepare graphics.
   c. construct the bibliography.
   d. interpret the findings.
   e. determine the physical format.

8. When you use statistical devices in a report, you should:
   a. let them stand separately.
   b. refer the reader to a standard statistical textbook.
   c. explain them.
   d. tell the reader how complicated the report is.
   e. show how they sophisticate the report.

9. The purpose of a report outline is to:
   a. force you to think about developing a logical plan to present the findings.
   b. provide a basis for a table of contents in a long report.
   c. provide a basis for the internal heading system.
   d. help keep you from forgetting some findings when you actually start writing.
   e. all of the above.

10. The major (first-level) divisions in a report outline are identified by:
    a. capital letters—A, B, C, etc.
    b. small letters—a, b, c, etc.
    c. Roman numerals—I, II, III, etc.
    d. Arabic numerals—1, 2, 3, etc.
    e. using parentheses—(1), (2), (3), etc. or (A), (B), (C), etc.

11. Starting with the most important, highest level and going to the lowest level, the conventional sequence of descending outline subdivision symbols is:
    a. A, I, a, 1, (a), (1).
    b. A, a, (a), I, 1, (1).
    c. I, (A), (1), (a), 1, a.
    d. I, A, 1, a, (1), (a).
    e. 1, A, I, (a), (I), a.

12. A report on the historical development of a company would logically be divided on the basis of:
    a. time.
    b. place.
    c. quantity.
    d. factors.
    e. hypotheses.

13. A report investigating differences in patterns of swimsuit sales in different climatic regions would be subdivided on the basis of:
    a. time.
    b. place.
    c. quantity.
    d. factors.
    e. hypotheses.

14. A report investigating different purchasing patterns of discretionary income on the basis of age and economic status would logically follow a breakdown of subdivisions on the basis of:
    a. time.
    b. place.
    c. quantity.
    d. factors.
    e. hypotheses.

15. Headings at any equal level:
    a. should be constructed as topic captions.
    b. should be constructed as talking captions.
    c. should be noun phrases.
    d. should be parallel in structure.
    e. may be mixed in form as long as they are equal in weight.

16. In deciding on what verb tense to use in your report, you should:
    a. use all present tense verbs (i.e., *is*).
    b. use all past tense verbs (i.e., *was*).
    c. be consistent in your use of time viewpoint.
    d. avoid future tense (*will be*) references.
    e. regard research findings as past tense.

17. One technique that helps a long report flow smoothly and increases readability is use of:
    a. the personal writing style.
    b. the same grammatical form for captions at all levels.
    c. the present verb tense throughout.
    d. transitional devices showing the relationships of succeeding parts of the writing.
    e. an interesting writing style that calls attention to itself.

Completion

1. Five key words or phrases that identify characteristics of reports are _____, _____, _____, _____, and _____.

2. A business report has its beginning in a need for _____ for a business purpose.

3. The first thing you need to do after being authorized to write a report is to _____.

4. In order to do this (see question 3), you will need to conduct a(n) _____.

5. Three ways to phrase a problem statement are (a) _____, (b) _____, and (c) _____.

6. The three types of problem factors are (a) _____, (b) _____, and (c) _____.

7. A problem that seeks an explanation or solution can be divided on the basis of _____, which can then be tested for correctness.

8. If the report problem requires you to interpret rather than merely present the facts, after you have collected the information for the report, you must _____ the findings by subtopics and then _____ _____ them and _____ them to the problem.

9. To help you organize the information for presentation of the report, you should prepare a(n) _____.

10. In a long report, the _____ forms the basis for the table of contents as well as being a guide for headings.

11. The three major parts of the report text are (a) _____, (b) _____, and (c) _____.

12. Simply said, outlining is a process of _____ the information you have gathered and interpreted so as to most effectively produce a logical approach to the problem.

13. Four bases for division of a report into parts of equal importance are (a) _____, (b) _____, (c) _____, and (d) _____.

14. In dividing by time, the divisions should be _____ in importance and _____ in length.

15. The _____ heading indicates what is going to be said about the subject, while the _____ heading simply identifies the topic of discussion.

Application Exercises

Exercise 1: Rearrange the following outline symbols to show a descending level of importance. Remember that if a topic has enough information to be subdivided with lower level headings , at least two lower level headings must appear in that subdivision.

A.

1.

I.

II.

2.

B.

b.

C.

c.

III.

a.

(1).

IV.

(2).

A.

a.

B.

b.

2.

1.

Exercise 2:

Part 1: Assume that you are writing a business report on results of a survey conducted to determine what styles of shoes are worn throughout the United States for various occasions by women of all ages. (The report will be used in developing an advertising-campaign strategy for your major shoe-manufacturing company.) What division possibilities exist (be specific)?

1) _____

2) _____

3) _____

4) _____

Part 2: Using three of the division possibilities you have chosen above, develop an outline with talking (popular) headings for the report you will write for the advertising manager. Use you imagination about specific findings. The first section is written out for you, and your final first-level caption will be the conclusions. Use first-, second-, and third-level headings.

I. Orientation to the Problem
   A. Authorization by Sales Manager
   B. Survey of Women's Patterns of Shoe Purchases
   C. Study of Company Sales Records
   D. Organization of the Findings

II.

Exercise 3: For each of the situations described below, identify the human error involved. Breifly comment on the correct interpretation procedure:

1. in reply to criticisms of the living conditions of his troops in a foreign encampment, an army general replied with some interesting statistical comparisons. One of these comparisons showed that the annual death rate of his men was less than 17 per 1,000—about the same as that for the capital city of the homeland.

2. A survey of smoking habits among college students revealed that grades made by nonsmokers were generally higher than theose made by heavy smokers. A conclusion that smoking caused low grades was reached.

3. A report on students in public elementary schools produced data showing that the health of the students was correlated with the grades they made. Grades of the students with defective eyes, ears, and teeth were found generally to be lower than grades of children without these defeats.

Report Structure: The Shorter Forms

13

Multiple Choice (Circle the best answer)

1. Longer and more formal reports typically use:
   a. more prefatory parts.
   b. a personal writing style.
   c. a title page, table of contents, and synopsis only.
   d. a title fly, table of contents, and letter of transmittal only.
   e. a similar structure to shorter, less formal reports.

2. Use of direct-order structure in reports follows the pattern of:
   a. introduction, analysis, conclusion.
   b. introduction, conclusion, analysis.
   c. analysis, introduction, conclusion.
   d. conclusion, introduction, analysis.
   e. conclusion, analysis, introduction.

3. Shorter reports:
   a. are more apt to deal with routine business operations.
   b. tend to use a more personal writing style.
   c. usually involve people who know each other.
   d. tend to have shorter headings.
   e. all of the above.

4. The short report structure:
   a. is seldom seen in business.
   b. consists of the title page and report text.
   c. always is written in the indirect order.
   d. follows letter format.
   e. uses impersonal style entirely.

5. Long and short reports both:
   a. use the same form of title page and page layout.
   b. always use impersonal writing style.
   c. have the same number of heading levels.
   d. always include bibliographies and graphics.
   e. always are in the direct order.

6. Letter reports:
   a. are usually written to a reader outside the company.
   b. usually are short (i.e., 3-4 pages).
   c. are written in personal style most of the time.
   d. may use a subject line to identify the report problem.
   e. all of the above.

7. A letter report follows an organizational plan similar to:
   a. direct routine letters.
   b. indirect refusal letters.
   c. indirect persuasive-request letters.
   d. attention-getting sales letters.
   e. longer, more formal report types.

8. Memorandum reports:
   a. are used extensively by firms for external communication.
   b. always use an impersonal writing style.
   c. always have introductory material.
   d. are often presented on standardized interoffice stationery.
   e. all of the above.

9. A memorandum report is apt to follow this format:
   a. title page, table of contents, report text.
   b. introduction, facts, summary.
   c. conclusion, introduction, analysis.
   d. date, to, from, subject, contents.
   e. date, salutation, subject line, recommendation.

10. The staff study report:
    a. differs from other reports in the organization of contents.
    b. ranges in length from memorandum to long and formal.
    c. leads systematically to conclusion and recommendation.
    d. is used mostly by the military forces.
    e. all of the above.

11. The most standardized of all report forms is probably the:
    a. long, formal report.
    b. short report.
    c. memorandum report.
    d. short-form audit report.
    e. technical report.

12. The technical report:
    a. differs primarily in subject matter from other reports.
    b. may vary in form used.
    c. usually begins with a title page and some prefatory parts.
    d. tends to follow a standard order similar to the staff study report.
    e. all of the above.

13. As a report becomes less formal, the first prefatory part apt to be dropped is the:
    a. salutation.
    b. letter of transmittal.
    c. title fly.
    d. executive summary.
    e. table of contents.

14. The least formal report most likely to deal with day-to-day problems is the:
    a. staff study report.
    b. audit report.
    c. memorandum report.
    d. letter report.
    e. short report.

15. The title page of a long or short report includes the following information:
    a. title, authorizing person, purpose.
    b. title, authorizing person, date.
    c. title, reader, writer, date.
    d. executive summary, letter of transmittal, writer, date.
    e. all of the above.

Completion

1. In a long, formal report, the body is preceded by prefatory parts which may include (a) _____, b) _____, (c) _____, (d) _____, and (e) _____.

2. The title page usually contains identification information such as (a) _____, (b) _____, (c) _____, and (d) _____.

3. The short report form commonly used in business contains only _____ and the _____.

4. The two least formal report forms used for short problems are the _____ and the _____.

5. The most commonly used reports in business are the _____ forms used for reporting _____ information.

6. The problem-solving-oriented short report form in business is likely to be written in the _____ order, which begins with _____.

7. Shorter reports are apt to use a more _____ writing style, while longer, more formal reports favor a(n) _____ style.

8. Short reports seldom use more than _____ level(s) of headings (subdivisions).

9. If you decide to write a letter report in the direct order, an effective way to quickly identify the report problem is to use a(n) _____ either before or after the salutation.

10. Letter reports are used primarily to present information to a reader _____ the company, while memorandum reports are used primarily for routine reporting _____ the company.

11. The least formal form of report is the _____.

12. Although staff study reports vary by company, they typically contain the following parts: (a) _____, (b) _____, (c) _____, (d) _____, (e) _____, and (f) _____.

13. A stereotyped statement often used by accountants is a(n) _____ report.

14. The main difference between technical reports and other reports is _____.

15. Staff study reports are probably used most often in _____.

Application Exercises

Exercise 1: Review Figure 13-1 in the text. Notice the major differences and similarities between the long, formal
Part 1:   report (1st step) and the short report (5th step). Using your imagination, construct an illustration
        (diagram, sketch) that will show these differences and similarities.

    Long, Formal   *Short*

Part 2:   Review Figures 13-2, 13-3, and 13-4. Note three areas of difference among the three shorter report
        forms below (steps 5-7 reports).

        Short Report   *Letter Report*   *Memorandum*

Identification of Parts
and/or Format:

Direct or Indirect:

Use of Captions:

Use of Graphics:

Exercise 2:   In four weeks, Gourmet Shoppes, Inc., will open its newest store in a new shopping mall in Middletown. The store will need a new manager and you are the one assigned the chore of finding that person.

For the past week you have been in Middletown screening applicants. In all, you interviewed 27. From this group you have selected what you consider to be the top three. Following company procedure, you will present all three to President Lois Anders. You will evaluate them on the criteria you consider important for the job, and you will rank them as you see them. You will present your findings in a memorandum addressed to President Anders.

A summary of the information you have gathered on each of the three follows:

Information	*Jay Monroe*	*Armand Gomez*	*Janet Keen*
Personal Information:	Age 27, married, 3 children, good health	Age 39, divorced, no children, service-connected disability but should not affect job performance	Age 29, married, one child
Experience:	3 yrs as attendant at J & M Service Station; 6 yrs with 24-Hour Food Stores, cashier, asst. manager (1 yr), and manager (3 yrs); currently employed by 24-Hour	20 yrs with Serve-Way Food Stores, duties as stock clerk, cashier, manager (7 yrs); currently employed by Serve-Way	3 yrs in real estate sales for Heights Co., 5 yrs with Morris Food Stores, asst. manager (2 yrs); currently employed by Morris
Education:	High School	High School; Center Business College (6-month course in office management)	High School; Middletown Community College (2-yr course in business administration)
Score on Management-Potential tests:*	80	87	94
Major Comments Made by References:	Very ambitious and hardworking. Tends to be quick-tempered but is fair. Has some run-ins with workers. Works employees hard. Honest and high morals.	A very gregarious person, well liked, personable. Somewhat easy on his subordinates. Honest. High morals. Meets public well.	Hardworking, honest, a taskmaster. Very intelligent. Works her subordinates hard. Ambitious. Occasionally has run-ins with her workers.

*Scores: grade of 60, passing; 75, average; 85+, excellent

TO: DATE:

FROM:

SUBJECT:

Long, Formal Reports

14

Multiple Choice (Circle the best answer)

1. Prefatory and appended parts are most apt to be used in the development of a(n):
   a. technical report.
   b. long, formal report.
   c. memorandum report.
   d. audit report.
   e. letter report.

2. The first of the prefatory parts to be dropped as a report decreases in length and formality is the:
   a. letter of authorization.
   b. letter of transmittal.
   c. title fly.
   d. executive summary.
   e. table of contents.

3. In order to construct a title for the report that tells at a glance the report's coverage yet is not excessively lengthy, you may need to:
   a. use a checklist that identifies *who* and *when*.
   b. answer the questions *what* and *where*.
   c. ask yourself the *why* and *how* questions in the problem.
   d. combine a broader title and a more specific subtitle.
   e. all of the above.

4. The major purpose of the title page is to:
   a. add formality.
   b. provide information necessary to identify the report.
   c. tell who asked for the report and who will use it.
   d. give the title and date it is recorded.
   e. all of the above.

5. One difference between a letter of transmittal and a foreword is:
   a. the letter of transmittal may use personal pronouns.
   b. the letter of transmittal may use conversational style.
   c. the foreword is not likely to be written on letterhead stationery.
   d. the foreword never attempts to summarize or interpret the material.
   e. the foreword is usually written in impersonal style.

6. A table of contents in a long report:
   a. repeats the outline headings.
   b. shows the reader where to find specific headings.
   c. helps readers who may not want to read the entire report to find the part(s) they want.
   d. lists some prefatory and appended parts as well as the text headings.
   e. all of the above.

7. Busy executives who may not have time to read the entire report are helped to find items of most interest to themselves in a long, formal report by using the:
   a. executive summary and table of contents.
   b. letter of transmittal and table of contents.
   c. title page and foreword.
   d. title fly and table of contents.
   e. title page and letter of authorization.

8. The executive summary may:
   a. include all major items of information.
   b. reduce the parts of the report in proportion.
   c. be about 1/8 the length of the actual report.
   d. use either direct or indirect order.
   e. all of the above.

9. In the introductory section, if you felt it necessary to define the exact coverage of the report problem, you would probably include a section on:
   a. origin.
   b. scope.
   c. limitations.
   d. historical background.
   e. definitions.

10. The introductory section describing how you collected the information for the report is called the:
    a. origin.
    b. scope.
    c. historical background.
    d. methodology.
    e. preview.

11. In long reports, the final section of the introduction is the report preview which covers:
    a. historical factors leading up to the problem.
    b. the sequence and logic of presentation of report.
    c. how long the report will be.
    d. what the expected findings will be.
    e. what will be covered in the appended parts.

12. The listing of major findings at the end of a report to present information is the:
    a. executive summary.
    b. summary.
    c. analysis.
    d. conclusion.
    e. recommendations.

13. Information that supplements material in the body of the report but does not logically fit within the report proper is included in a(n):
    a. executive summary.
    b. table of illustrations.
    c. summary.
    d. appendix.
    e. bibliography.

14. To tie a long report together smoothly, structural aids to coherence:
    a. help the reader relate the parts of the report.
    b. begin with the preview section in the introduction.
    c. include introductory and summary sections at the beginnings and ends of major divisions.
    d. form a network of connection throughout the report.
    e. all of the above.
15. Which of the following is *not* illustrated in the long, formal report shown in Figure 14-3 in your text?
    a. Three-spot title page
    b. Letter of authorization
    c. Table of illustrations
    d. Executive summary
    e. Graphics

Completion

1. The more formal a report, the larger the number of _____ that are likely to be included.

2. The contents of the title fly page contain _____.

3. The report title needs to be built around the questions _____, _____, _____, _____, _____, and sometimes _____ in order to describe the report precisely.

4. One way to balance completeness and conciseness in constructing a report title is through the use of _____ _____.

5. One part of the report not written by the report writer is _____.

6. In a combined letter of transmittal and executive summary, you would write in _____ form, beginning in the _____ order, following with _____, and closing with _____.

7. The prefatory part that gives the report in miniature is called the _____.

8. When the report proper begins with the conclusion, with the introduction second and body third, it is said to be written in the _____ order.

9. The part of the report designed to familiarize the reader with the background of the problem is called the _____.

10. In a long report, information about who authorized the report may be included either in a(n) _____ as one of the prefatory parts or in the _____ of the _____ of the report.

11. Explanation about insufficient time, a very limited budget, or lack of access to needed sources of information should be given in a section on _____.

12. A "road map" to the sequential unfolding of the report itself is usually included in the _____ as a final part of the introduction.

13. Recommendation(s) should be used to end a report only if the readers _____.

14. Appended parts after the end of the report body generally include _____ and/or _____.

15. If your report information comes mostly from published (secondary) sources you found in periodicals, books, etc., at libraries, you need to list these sources in a(n) _____ after the final section of the report proper.

Application Exercises

Assume that you are working for the Yankee Textile Company in its Boston executive office. Yankee is in the process of locating a new textile mill in the Texas wool-producing area. So far, Yankee has narrowed the selection to five towns: Ballinger, Big Spring, Coleman, Littlefield, and San Marcos. You have been assigned the task of gathering all pertinent data on the towns, making appropriate comparisons, and recommending a choice. The report that will present your work is outlined in your textbook (p. 394).

Part 1:   Using the information above, the outline in your book, and your logical imagination to supply any additional information you may need, list the 5 *Ws* and *How* that should be considered in constructing the title.

Who: _____

What: _____

When: _____

Where: _____

Why: _____

How: _____

Next, evaluate the need for each, and construct an appropriate title for this report.

_____

_____

_____

_____

_____

_____

Part 2:   Using the location problem described on the previous page, write the preview section of the introduction (part I, D in the outline).

Part 3:   For the same problem, write the introductory paragraph to section III of the outline.

Part 4:   Write the paragraph that summarizes your findings in section III of this report. You will need to follow the information given in the outline. You may also use your logical imagination if necessary.

Graphics

15

Multiple Choice (Circle the best answer)

1. Graphics are useful in presenting information that:
   a. deserves special emphasis.
   b. is too detailed to be covered in words.
   c. is so complex that visual presentation can clarify it.
   d. summarizes masses of detail more compactly.
   e. all of the above.

2. In a report, graphics should be:
   a. grouped at the end of the report.
   b. grouped at the end of each major section.
   c. near where they are first mentioned in the written material.
   d. placed in the appendix.
   e. always placed at the top of a page of written material.

3. For a graphic showing only two or three qualities or factors, an appropriate size might be:
   a. 1/4 page.
   b. 1/2 page.
   c. a full page.
   d. a fold-out page.
   e. whatever space is left over on the page after it is typed.

4. In numbering graphics:
   a. all illustrations should use Roman numerals.
   b. each different type of graphic must be numbered separately.
   c. all graphics other than tables may be grouped together.
   d. tables always are numbered separately with Arabic numerals.
   e. it is simplest to number tables and other graphics according to the page they are on.

5. The caption title for the graphic should consider _____ in describing the contents of the graphic to the reader.
   a. who
   b. what
   c. where and why
   d. when and how
   e. all of the above

6. Titles for graphics conventionally appear:
   a. at the top of the illustration.
   b. at the bottom of the illustration.
   c. at the top of the illustration for tables and at the bottom for figures.
   d. at the top of the illustration for figures and at the bottom for tables.
   e. in all capital letters to set them off from text material.

7. Tables differ from other illustration forms in that they:
   a. always present data in an orderly arrangement.
   b. always present information in horizontal rows.
   c. always present information in vertical columns.
   d. identify units in which the data are recorded.
   e. are not truly pictures.

8. In constructing a bar chart, you need to remember to:
   a. make each bar of equal width.
   b. identify each bar with a caption.
   c. identify magnitudes of the bars on the grid.
   d. always arrange the bars vertically.
   e. all but d.

9. Simple bar charts are used to:
   a. compare differences in quantities by lengths of the bars.
   b. compare groups of two or three different kinds of quantities over time.
   c. show plus and minus differences.
   d. compare divisions of a whole.
   e. present data in an orderly arrangement of rows and columns.

10. Pie charts and sometimes subdivided bar charts are used to:
   a. compare differences in quantities by lengths of the bars.
   b. compare groups of two or three different kinds of quantities over time.
   c. show plus and minus differences.
   d. compare divisions of a whole.
   e. present data in an orderly arrangement of rows and columns.

11. If you need to show both positive and negative values in a graphic, you can use a:
   a. multiple bar chart.
   b. bilateral bar chart.
   c. subdivided bar chart.
   d. line chart.
   e. pictogram.

12. If you want to show change across time both by subdivisions and total quantity, you can use:
   a. multiple-bar charts.
   b. bilateral bar charts.
   c. line charts with multiple series.
   d. either a subdivided bar chart or a component-part line chart.
   e. a pie chart or pictogram.

13. Of the following graphic forms, _____ do *not* lend themselves to showing changes across time.
   a. tables
   b. simple bar charts
   c. subdivided bar charts
   d. pie charts
   e. line charts

14. A pie chart:
    a. shows divisions of a whole (100 percent) as proportional-size "slices" or wedges of a circle.
    b. should alternate large and small slices for easier comparison.
    c. should begin "slicing the pie" at the six o'clock position.
    d. can be drawn in a series of sizes to show differences in total volumes.
    e. is usually superimposed on a grid.

15. Communicating quantitative information in a quickly grasped visual form is the purpose in all of the following except the:
    a. drawing.
    b. pictogram.
    c. statistical map.
    d. pie chart.
    e. component-part line.

Completion

1. The use and purpose of graphics should be based on the _____.

2. Summary tables that help meet the need for completeness but are not actually discussed in the text of a report are sometimes placed _____.

3. The size of a graphic should be based on _____.

4. When a graphic is less than a full page in size, you should place _____ to set it off from the text material.

5. Two techniques used in constructing graphics to help the reader see distinctions and comparisons are _____ and _____.

6. For numbering purposes, illustrations should be divided into at least two distinct groupings: (a) _____ _____ and (b) _____.

7. Identification of the person, agency, or authority that gathered the data cited in an illustration is given in a(n) _____.

8. Information displayed in an orderly arrangement of rows and columns rather than pictorially is referred to as _____.

9. The main parts of a bar chart are the _____ and the _____.

10. Whether arranged horizontally or vertically, it is vitally important that all bars on the grid be _____ _____.

11. Bar charts compare differences in quantities by their varying _____.

12. In a multiple-bar chart or a subdivided bar chart, you may use a(n) _____ to distinguish different kinds of information coded according to different colors, shades, or crosshatching.

13. A line chart shows change of information over time by using a(n) _____ plotted on a grid showing time changes from left-to-right on the _____ and quantity changes on a vertical _____.

14. To avoid visual confusion, a practical rule is to avoid using more than _____ comparisons on a multiple-bar chart or _____ lines on a line chart.

15. Three rules you should remember in correctly constructing a line chart are (a) _____ _____ (b) _____, and (c) _____.

Application Exercises

Exercise 1: You arc writing a report on the type of firms that have been your company's major customers in the past six months. From the following table, construct two graphics you will use in a presentation to your sales supervisors.

Company Size in Number of Employees	Type of Company				
	Manufacturing	Wholesaling	Retailing	Service	Total
1–15	6	7	20	14	47
16–50	5	17	14	16	52
51–100	4	9	3	8	24
100+	7	4	14	13	38
Total	22	37	51	51	161

First, develop a pie chart to show the relative numbers of firms you sell to by size (in terms of numbers of employees). *Hint:* You must divide 47 by 161 (the total number of companies) to learn what percentage of companies have 1–15 employees (29 percent). Then since a circle is 360°, you need to multiply 360 by 0.29 to learn that 105° of the circle is the "slice of the pie" representing companies with 1–15 employees.

Figure _____: _____ (title)

Second, develop a simple bar chart to compare the types of companies (manufacturing, wholesaling, retailing, and service) that are your customers. You must use numbers, not percentages.

Figure _____: _____ (title)

Exercise 2: You are developing a report on grade inflation at your school. In this case you want to show changes in the GPAs over the past five years by comparing the percent of grades given by letter (A, B, C D, F, other). Prepare the appropriate graphics to do this.

Percent of Grades Earned in Each Grade Grouping

	Last Year	2 Yrs Ago	3 Yrs Ago	4 Yrs Ago	5 Yrs Ago
A	24.0	23.8	23.7	23.3	21.9
B	32.2	32.7	32.6	32.6	34.3
C	26.5	26.9	27.6	28.2	29.2
D	8.8	8.5	8.5	8.9	8.3
F	6.6	6.1	5.9	6.0	5.3
W	2.0	1.9	1.7	1.1	1.1

Informal Oral Communication

16

Multiple Choice (Circle the best answer)

1. Which of the following is not an element of good talking as discussed in the text:
   a. voice quality
   b. talking style
   c. word choice
   d. adaptation
   e. filtering

2. In talking to three subordinates on an assembly line, you make the following statement: "If you continue to make parts that are too long, I will dock you $2.00 for each one." Your statement is an example of:
   a. voice quality
   b. pitch
   c. voice style
   d. adaptation
   e. volume

3. Which of the following instructions is *not* one of the ten commandments of good listening?
   a. Show the talker you want to listen.
   b. Put the talker on the defensive.
   c. Hold your temper.
   d. Ask questions.
   e. Be patient.

4. It is estimated that after two days we remember only _____ of what we heard.
   a. 10%
   b. 25%
   c. 33%
   d. 50%
   e. 75%

5. Probably the weakest link in oral communication for most people is in:
   a. listening.
   b. dictating letters.
   c. interviewing.
   d. making speeches.
   e. conducting informal meetings.

6. Which of the following statements best describes the nature of nonverbal communication?
   a. Nonverbal communication is precise and specific.
   b. Nonverbal communication is more specific than verbal communication.
   c. Nonverbal communication is the same thing as body language.
   d. Nonverbal communication conveys the same meanings across different cultures.
   e. Nonverbal communication is broad and imprecise.

7. If one of the following is not a type of nonverbal communication, mark it. If all are types, mark (e).
   a. Gestures
   b. Smiles
   c. Space
   d. Telephone calls
   e. All are types of nonverbal communication.

8. In conducting an interview, the interviewer should:
   a. predetermine the information needs of the interview.
   b. keep the interviewee nervous and slightly off balance.
   c. keep the interviewee guessing about the purpose of the interview unless it is obvious.
   d. do most of the talking.
   e. always avoid taking notes during the interview itself.

9. An interviewer needs to:
   a. plan questions that lead to gaining the information desired.
   b. listen carefully.
   c. give the appearance of interested listening.
   d. plan a tactful way to end the interview.
   e. do all of the above.

10. If you are the interviewee for a job, you need to:
    a. try to anticipate the questions you will be asked and plan answers.
    b. try to learn something about the company in advance.
    c. dress for the situation is a way that gives the best impression.
    d. answer questions completely, honestly, and politely.
    e. do all of the above.

11. If you are in charge of conducting a meeting, it is up to you to:
    a. understand parliamentary procedure, particularly if the meeting is formal.
    b. plan an agenda arranged in logical order.
    c. keep the meeting on track and not let it stray from the agenda.
    d. allow for adequate discussion without letting new items or excessive details detract from the meeting's goals.
    e. all of the above.

12. When a participant in a meeting dominates discussion without contributing much to the goal, the person conducting the meeting should:
    a. let the person continue so that the meeting will be democratic.
    b. tactfully step in by asking for other viewpoints or summarizing and moving to the next topic.
    c. cut the person off with a request to stop talking.
    d. explain that the person is dominating the discussion.
    e. ask the group if they want to hear more from this person.

13. The best of the following suggestions to encourage shy participants to talk at a meeting is for the leader to:
    a. announce that some people are not participating.
    b. reprimand the people for not participating.
    c. lecture the group on the need to participate.
    d. ask these people for their viewpoints.
    e. call out the names of those not participating.

14. When you are a participant in a meeting and another participant talks at length on an item not on the agenda, you should:
    a. make no comment on the item.
    b. ask the leader to silence this participant.
    c. inform this participant that he or she is out of order.
    d. ask the group to censure this participant.
    e. give your viewpoints on the item.

15. As a participant in a meeting, it is up to you to:
    a. bring up important items that accidentally may have been left out of the agenda.
    b. have something to contribute on every topic.
    c. ask the leader to summarize the key points at the end of each topic if he or she forgets.
    d. be polite and cooperate on time limitations.
    e. all of the above are desirable.

16. Which of the following beginning comments is best for one originating a routine business telephone call?
    a. "Joan Barr here. Calling Hal Hinton."
    b. "I want Hal Hinton."
    c. "I am calling Hinton."
    d. "Hal Hinton there?"
    e. "This is Joan Barr of Barr Associates. May I speak with Hal Hinton, please."

17. Mark the best of these telephone responses by a secretary. The secretary's boss is not in.
    a. "Sorry, Smith can't talk now."
    b. "You'll have to call back. Smith's not here."
    c. "She's out of the office. Sorry."
    d. "Ms. Smith is not in right now. May I ask her to return your call?"
    e. "Who is calling, please?"

18. Before you dictate a letter or short report, you need to:
    a. gather all the information.
    b. develop an outline.
    c. rehearse, especially if you are not accustomed to dictating.
    d. tell the stenographer the complete address, and give any special instructions relative to the communication.
    e. do all of the above.

Completion

1. Whenever you vary pitch, change speed, and alternate volume in talking, you are practicing _____ _____.

2. Talking style refers to the blending of _____, _____, and _____ plus _____.

3. As in writing, the best that a receiver/listener can say after hearing someone speak is "_____."

4. Improving your ability to listen is largely a matter of _____ _____.

5. The first commandment of effective listening is to _____ _____. The tenth commandment is to _____.

6. The four types of space we use to communicate are these: _____, _____, _____, and _____.

7. Of all the body features, the _____ and _____ convey most of the meaning in body language.

8. Interviews are conducted in business for these purposes:
   (1) _____, (2) _____, and (3) _____.

9. The one who should do most of the talking in a good interview is the _____.

10. One good way for the interviewer to end the interview is to ask a _____.

11. When you participate in a business conference, your role will be that of either _____ or _____.

12. Very formal meetings are likely to follow strict procedures such as the rules of _____, _____ for which special guidebooks are available.

13. The list of topics to be discussed in a meeting is called the _____.

14. When conducting a meeting in which time is limited, you should _____ and _____.

15. When conducting a meeting you may need to summarize after _____ and at _____.

16. When as a participant in a meeting you want to comment on an item not on the agenda, you should _____ _____.

17. Best advice for developing a friendly telephone voice is to _____ _____.

18. At the beginning of a telephone conversation that you have initiated, it is good practice to _____ _____.

19. In most dictation cases, you will need to handle paragraphing, punctuation, and other mechanics by _____ _____.

20. In preparing to dictate a letter, your first step should be to _____ in order to avoid interruptions later.

Application Exercises

Exercise 1 (Meetings):

Your instructor will select a meeting topic from the list under "Meetings" at the end of Chapter 16. You and your classmates will develop plans for this meeting. Then your instructor will select one class member to serve as leader. Using his or her plan, this meeting leader will conduct the meeting with the class members serving as participants. All class members should work to make the meeting as realistic as possible. During the meeting you and your classmates will note on the following forms any good or bad participation observed. After the meeting all of you will discuss your observations.

Criticism of the Leader

The Meeting Plan	How Well the Plan Was Followed	How Well the Discussion was Moved Along

Leader's Control of Participants	Encouragement of Nonparticipants to Participate

Adherence to the Agenda	Extent of Participation	

Dominant Talkers	Cooperative Attitude	Courtesy

Exercise 2 (Interviewing):

Each class member will plan for an employment interview for the position of management trainee with a major local company. The planning should be for the roles of interviewer and interviewee. Then your instructor will select one class member as interviewer and another as interviewee. These two people will conduct the interview with the other class members serving as observers. Using the form below, the observers will take notes on the performance of the participants. Following the interview, the class will discuss the notes taken and make recommendations to the participants.

Interviewer

Planning	How Well Interviewee Placed at Ease	Extent of Talking
How Interview Guided	How Record of Interview Kept	How Well Interview Ended

Interviewee

Evidence of Preparation	Appearance	Display of Interest
Quality of Answers		Courtesy

Exercise 3 (Dictation):

Working with a classmate, select one of the letter problems at the end of Chapter 5. Think it through and plan your letter. Then dictate your letter to your classmate, who will record your dictation in longhand. Next, reverse the roles. Exchange criticisms and suggestions. (Your instructor may want to evaluate the dictated work.)

Exercise 4 (Telephone):

Imagine this situation for a telephone conversation. Grace Kite, sales manager for Bacha Plumbing Wholesale Company, wants to talk to William Huggins, president of Huggins Plumbing, Inc., about a new line of bathroom fixtures Bacha has acquired. Ms. Kite calls Mr. Huggins's offices, and the secretary answers. Mr. Huggins is out for the day and will be back in the morning. The secretary assumes that he will want to talk with Ms. Kite.

Your instructor will select two class members to simulate this telephone call. One will play the role of Ms. Kite and the other the role of the secretary. The other class members will observe and take notes on the good points and bad points they detect. After the call has ended, the class will discuss the good and bad points observed.

Exercise 5 (Nonverbal):

Select one of the oral report topics on pages 613-614 of your text. Prepare an outline of the content of the report. In your outline, insert what types of nonverbal communication you would use. Justify their use in your report.

Public Speaking and Oral Reporting

17

Multiple Choice (Circle the best answer)

1. Probably the most difficult kind of oral communication in doing your job is going to be:
   a. participation in a committee meeting.
   b. telephone calls with prospective customers.
   c. group discussion on implementing new programs.
   d. formal presentations (i.e., a speech) before groups.
   e. interviews with job applicants.

2. In order to make a good speech before a group, you should:
   a. be thoroughly familiar with the material you present.
   b. rehearse.
   c. analyze yourself as a speaker.
   d. analyze your audience.
   e. all of the above.

3. The organization of a business speech is most likely to be by:
   a. time.
   b. place.
   c. quantity.
   d. factor.
   e. distance.

4. The most popular and effective method of presenting a speech is:
   a. extemporaneous presentation.
   b. memorizing.
   c. reading.
   d. writing.
   e. tape recording.

5. To give a successful presentation, you need to:
   a. speak in a clear, strong voice (not shout or whisper).
   b. dress carefully.
   c. strike a balance between thorough coverage and too much detail.
   d. project friendliness.
   e. all of the above.

6. As you speak, your audience is aware of:
   a. your personal appearance.
   b. "body language" (i.e., gestures).
   c. the stage, lighting, and background.
   d. outside noises.
   e. all of the above.

7. Vocal qualities that can enhance a speech's effectiveness include:
    a. speaking in a monotone.
    b. varying speaking speed.
    c. talking slowly at a uniform rate.
    d. pausing frequently and filling in with "you know" or "OK?"
    e. keeping voice volume consistent throughout.

8. Major points in a speech may be emphasized through:
    a. varying speaking speed.
    b. speaking louder or softer.
    c. using pause selectively.
    d. using visuals.
    e. all of the above.

9. The best advice in using visuals to emphasize the major points in an oral presentation is:
    a. use visuals that fit the one speech and the one audience.
    b. use a slide projector.
    c. use a flip chart.
    d. use a combined flip chart for graphs and tables, and use the blackboard.
    e. use video tapes and/or samples and demonstrations.

10. Mark the suggestion that is *not* appropriate in the use of visuals in a speech.
    a. Point to the visuals; emphasize them.
    b. Explain them as much as necessary.
    c. Look directly at the visuals while explaining them.
    d. Avoid blocking the listener's view of the visual.
    e. Make certain all in the audience can see the visuals.

11. An oral report:
    a. has an advantage over the written report in that it permits greater use of visuals to communication.
    b. allows the speaker to set the pace of the communication.
    c. allows the listener to control the pace of the communication.
    d. requires a greater degree of correctness than the written report.
    e. always allows a less formal presentation than the written report.

12. The major difference in the organization of oral and written reports is in the:
    a. introduction.
    b. transactions.
    c. ending.
    d. presentation of findings.
    e. use of visuals.

13. The logical procedure for planning a formal oral report is:
    a. the same as it is for the formal written report.
    b. to clearly state the report goal.
    c. to decide on the factors necessary for attaining the goal.
    d. to remain aware of the general purpose in making the report.
    e. all of the above.

14. The logical organization of material for presentation of the oral report:
    a. is always the same as for a written report.
    b. uses indirect order most often.
    c. is less likely than the written to need a final summary.
    d. uses a synopsis at the beginning even in a relatively informal situation.
    e. all of the above.

Completion

1. Your first step in formal speech making is to _____.

2. In your search for a speech topic, you would do well to be guided by _____ and _____.

3. The organization of a formal speech usually begins with _____.

4. The introduction of a speech resembles that of a written report, but often it has the additional need to _____.

5. The inductive (indirect) order is appropriate for a speech when your goal is to _____ _____.

6. The major personal aspects you should consider in speech making are _____, _____, and _____.

7. in preparing your speech, you need to consider characteristics of your prospective audience. For example, ask yourself about audience (a) _____, (b) _____, (c) _____, (d) _____, and (e) _____ in order to effectively adapt your presentation to the group.

8. Even while you are actually giving your speech, you need to continually consider _____ from the audience.

9. When you make a formal presentation your audience will form impressions from these factors: _____, _____, _____, _____, _____, and _____.

10. It is important and natural to vary pitch or tone in your voice. Thus, you should not talk _____ _____.

11. A modern-day device you can use privately to help yourself improve your speaking ability is a(n) _____ _____.

12. Your selection of a form of visual for use in a speech should be made primarily on the basis of _____ _____.

13. An oral report may be defined as an _____ _____. A business oral report limits coverage to _____ _____.

14. The three primary differences between written and oral reports are:
    (1) _____,
    (2) _____,
    and (3) _____.

15. Your first step in planning the oral report is to determine _____

_____.

16. The major difference in the organization of oral and written reports is that oral reports are more likely to have _____.

Application Exercise

Prepare a ten-minute speech or oral report on a topic assigned by your instructor. Your instructor will select one (or more) of yo to present your speech before the class. As one of your classmates makes his or her presentation, evaluate the performance on the basis of the points discussed in the chapter. Mark your observation notes on the forms below.

After making the evaluation, discuss your comments with other class members and give consensus to the speaker.

Organization

Introduction, (interests, Adequacy, Theme)	Body (Logic, Coherence, Completeness, etc.)	Ending (Subject restatement, Summary, Conclusion)

Personal Aspects

Confidence (in Self and in Audience)	Sincerity	Thoroughness	Friendliness

Appearance, Bodily Actions

Personal Appearance	Posture	Walking

Facial Expression	Gestures

Voice

Quality	Pitch Variation
Speed	**Vocal Emphasis**

Use of Visuals

Appropriateness	Technique of Using

Special Topic: Technology-Assisted Communication

18

Multiple Choice (Circle the best answer)

1. Computer technology helps the writer:
   a. in only the writing step of the process.
   b. in both the writing and revising steps of the process.
   c. in both the collecting and writing steps of the process.
   d. in all steps of the writing process.
   e. predominantly in the analysis step of the process.

2. Which one of the tools listed below helps writers most in the planning of a long document?
   a. Word Processing
   b. Database
   c. Spreadsheet
   d. Personal Information Managers
   e. Project Management

3. With communications software and a modem, writers can gather information from external sources such as:
   a. library card catalogs.
   b. private online services.
   c. other companies' computers.
   d. other PCs with modems and the correct software.
   e. All of the above.

4. Which of the tools listed below is not one writers find useful in analyzing data?
   a. Graphics
   b. Statistics
   c. Project management
   d. Spreadsheet
   e. All of the above are useful.

5. How is the search and replace feature of word processing software used when writing documents?
   a. To search the a particular word and replace it with another word.
   b. To search for a particular spot marked and replace it with new material.
   c. To search for a file on the disk and replace the current file with it.
   d. Both a and b.
   e. None of the above.

6. Which feature would you use to smooth a particularly ragged right margin of a document using a fixed pitch typeface?
   a. Right justification
   b. Left justification
   c. Full justification
   d. Hyphenation
   e. None of the above.

7. The merge feature allows the writer to combine a form document with another document containing variables. A particularly good application of this feature would be:
   a. in a special document to a single but special supplier.
   b. in a special report.
   c. in early and late stage collection letters.
   d. Both a and b.
   e. None of the above.

8. A recent study found spell checkers missed 25 percent of the errors students made. Which of the errors listed below would a spell checker miss?
   a. Everyone felt the earthquake last night accept Marina.
   b. The vice president misspelled the word potatoe.
   c. Please give the totals thru June.
   d. Joan's birhtday is April 9.
   e. None of the above.

9. Use of white space is one of the basic principles of layout. For improved readability, a commonly accepted ratio of white space to text is:
   a. 1:8
   b. 1:5
   c. 1:3
   d. 1:1
   e. 2:3

10. A graphic device used to emphasize text is:
    a. a shaded box.
    b. a ruled box.
    c. a pull quote.
    d. white space.
    e. All of the above.

11. Publishing professionals use which of the following terms to refer to the vertical adjusting space.
    a. Points and picas
    b. Pitch
    c. Leading
    d. Kerning
    e. Font

12. In circumstances where you must have the best-looking output, you would choose which of the following?
    a. Typesetting
    b. Dot matrix printing
    c. Laser
    d. Inkjet
    e. Either c or d

13. The growth rate of electronic mail use has been increasing rapidly. This is often attributed to its use on which of the following systems?
    a. Mainframe computers
    b. Minicomputers
    c. Local area networks (LANs)
    d. Bulletin board systems (BBSs)
    e. All of the above.

14. A synchronous tool used for collaborative writing is often referred to as electronic meeting systems. An advantage of this tool is that it improves group work by:
    a. providing an equal opportunity for participation.
    b. permitting groups to use a variety of tools as needed.
    c. discouraging behavior that negatively impacts meetings.
    d. enabling a large number of ideas to be managed effectively.
    e. All of the above.

Completion

1. Technology assists the writer with both the _____ and _____ writing tasks.

2. A tool that helps writers plan time to set aside for writing is _____.

3. Database software provides a convenient way to collect information so that you can _____ it when it's needed.

4. Identify five tools other than word processing that writers use during the writing step of the writing process.
   (1) _____ (2) _____ (3)_____
   (4) _____ (5) _____

5. Most full featured word processing programs have two features that will let the writer add columns and rows of information. These features are _____ and _____.

6. _____ art allows writers to put ready-made art easily into documents.

7. To breakout of the typewriter era, writers use _____ to present professional-looking documents.

8. Three basic design principles that are important to writes are (1) _____, (2) _____, and (3) _____.

9. When layout works well, it works well with _____ and _____.

10. Identify two technologies for transmitting oral messages that have come into wide use only within the last three to five years.
    (1)_____
    (2) _____

---

11. Transmitting documents by facsimile is _____, _____, and _____.

12. There are two classifications of tools used for collaborative writing. These are (1) _____ and (2) _____.

Application Exercise

Select an office about which you can get information—your school, the company where you work, a company where a friend or acquaintance works. Describe the use of the computer tools in this office. Note how they compare to some of the uses you have learned about here.

Special Topic: Techniques of International Communication

19

Multiple Choice (Circle the best answer)

1. Assume that while visiting a foreign land you observed a native waving a clinched fist above his head. This gesture signifies:
   a. defiance and/or anger.
   b. cooperation.
   c. happiness.
   d. ? (depends on where you are, for meanings vary by culture)
   e. a show of strength or power.

2. Which of these statements expresses the most accurate evaluation of our culture's view of time as something to be planned for and used efficiently?
   a. Highly superior to other viewpoints
   b. Different, but not necessarily superior
   c. Highly inferior to other viewpoints
   d. Superior to some views, inferior to others
   e. Slightly superior to other viewpoints

3. Our techniques of letter writing:
   a. are effective with people from all cultures.
   b. are effective with all English-speaking people.
   c. are effective with Japanese readers.
   d. should be avoided completely in writing to foreigners.
   e. should be modified to the culture of a foreign reader.

4. The major reason(s) for difficulty in making precisely equivalent translations among languages is (are):
   a. the different concepts, views, etc. cultures have.
   b. errors in dictionaries.
   c. grammatical and syntactical differences.
   d. the problem of multiple meanings of words.
   e. variations in the alphabets used.

5. Mark the sentence that is most likely to communicate with a foreign reader.
   a. Our secretary has gone to her reward.
   b. Our secretary passed away.
   c. Our secretary died.
   d. Our secretary kicked the bucket.
   e. Our secretary checked out.

6. Which of these sentences is most likely to be understood by a foreigner?
   a. He balked at our offer.
   b. The equipment is worth twenty grand.
   c. We will have to write off the loss.
   d. He will pay you $20,000 for this machinery.
   e. Your quick response caught us flat-footed.

7. Mark the sentence that is most likely to communicate with a foreign reader.
   a. We will stop negotiations.
   b. We will break off negotiations.
   c. We will cut off negotiations.
   d. We will pull out of the negotiations.
   e. We will clear out of the negotiations.

Completion

1. You can overcome the cultural differences that cause communication problems by _____
   _____.

2. *Culture* may be defined as _____
   _____.

3. People of a culture tend to view their ways as _____ and the ways of other cultures as
   _____.

4. An up-and-down movement of the head means _____ to us but _____
   to people of other cultures.

5. People from different cultures view space between people differently. For example, North Americans prefer
   _____ between themselves and those with whom they talk; some Asians prefer
   _____.

6. Differing attitudes toward these five factors of human relationships are the causes of much miscommunication among people of different cultures: (1) _____, (2) _____,
   (3) _____, (4) _____, (5) _____.

7. Words such as *run, cat,* and *trip* cause problems in translation because _____.

8. The translating procedure using two translators, each an expert in one of the languages involved, is called
   _____.

9. Wordings such as *keep away, play down, give in,* and *take off* are difficult for foreigners. We call these wordings _____.

10. Three culturally derived groups of words that should be avoided in communicating with foreigners are
    (1) _____, (2) _____, and (3) _____.

11. One general suggestion for communicating in English with foreigners is to talk (or write) _____
    _____ and _____.

Application Exercise

For each of the following paragraphs, underline the wordings that probably would be difficult for a foreign reader to understand.

1. Today I was able to pin down our sales manager and get the enclosed price quotations. As I promised, I went to bat for you and got him to make you a honey of a deal. The Cory work shoes are a steal at $31.50. I hope you are able to cash in on these bargains.

2. Ms. Keyser said that she was fed up with our service. Unless we shape up soon, she will cancel our contract. I want you to check out the situation and see what is driving her up the wall. Touch base with me when you have something to report.

Special Topic: Physical Presentation of Reports and Letters

20

Multiple Choice (Circle the best answer)

1. Close attention to the correct physical presentation of a letter, memorandum, or report is important because:
   a. it helps create a positive image of the writer and the company.
   b. it gives an impression of competence.
   c. it can affect how successfully the document message is received.
   d. it shows respect for the reader.
   e. all of the above.

2. Unless the font you are using in your document is proportional, you should set your justification to:
   a. left.
   b. right.
   c. full.
   d. full with hyphenation on.
   e. Any of the above.

3. The most widely used media today is:
   a. paper.
   b. floppy disk.
   c. E-mail.
   d. fax.
   e. optical disk.

4. You are writing a letter to Linda Smythe, a female executive whom you have never met, and you do not know if she is married or what title she prefers. You should begin the salutation:
   a. Dear Miss Smythe:
   b. Dear Mrs. Smythe:
   c. Dear Ms. Smythe:
   d. Dear Linda:
   e. Dear Madam:

5. Additional notations after the signature block that may be appropriate on occasion include:
   a. ENC.
   b. LS:jb
   c. cc:
   d. P.S.
   e. all of the above.

6. Proper margins on a report page:
   a. need to be equal on sides, top, and bottom.
   b. need to be the same at top and bottom.
   c. should be about 1" for single-spaced manuscripts.
   d. should be about 1 1/4" to 1 1/2" for double-spaced manuscripts.
   e. should allow an extra half-inch on the left margin for binding.

7. The bottom margin should be:
   a. the same as the top.
   b. the same as the sides.
   c. about 2" on special pages (i.e., where a page starts with title of chapter).
   d. about 1 1/2 times the size of the other margins, allowing for binding.
   e. deep enough to allow for 1" after the page number is typed in.

8. On the title page, the title itself should:
   a. appear slightly above the vertical center.
   b. observe the requirements of the 5 *Ws* and *how* in wording.
   c. be typed in the highest ranking type used in the report.
   d. be centered.
   e. b, c, and d.

9. The report outline, which you developed earlier as you were researching and writing the report:
   a. is now the basis for the table of contents.
   b. is now the basis for the heading system.
   c. should be included in rough-draft form in an appendix.
   d. can now be forgotten, as it has done its job.
   e. serves the dual purpose of both a and b.

10. The table of illustrations must:
    a. be a separate table.
    b. be a continuation of the table of contents.
    c. list tables and other graphic aids separately.
    d. have an exactly even left margin.
    e. follow the figure or table number immediately with the page number.

11. In typing the report manuscript, you should:
    a. always double-space for ease in reading.
    b. always single-space so it looks more like a printed report.
    c. triple-space above and below all centered heads.
    d. always indent the first line of a paragraph eight spaces.
    e. either a or b.

12. Pages should be numbered:
    a. consecutively with Arabic numerals starting immediately after the title page.
    b. with small Roman numerals for the prefatory parts and Arabic numerals for the text.
    c. with small Roman numerals for the prefatory or appended parts and Arabic numerals for the report proper.
    d. in the upper right corner always.
    e. at the bottom center always.

13. Report headings can give the reader an indication of the relative importance of the report part they head by:
    a.   how the heading is formed (typeface, size, style).
    b.   how the heading is positioned (centered or on the margin).
    c.   whether the heading is underscored.
    d.   none of the above.
    e.   Both a and b.

Completion

1. All documents require basic decisions on (a) _____, (b) _____, and (c) _____.

2. Surrounding text or a graphic with external white space has the effect of giving it _____.

3. Adjusting vertical spacing is called _____; adjusting horizontal spacing is called _____.

4. Sans serif typeface characters have no feet and are best for presenting legible _____; serif typeface characters have feet and are best for _____.

5. Type is measured in points. Body type is usually _____ to _____ points while headings are _____ points or larger.

6. The purpose served by the margins on a letter or report page is similar to that of a(n) _____ for a picture.

7. The _____ margin is straight, although the _____ margin may vary slightly according to the length of the typed line.

8. The two most popular layout styles for typing letters are _____ style and _____ style.

9. Except for extremely short letters, spacing within a paragraph is _____ and _____ between paragraphs.

10. If the letter is longer than one page, the following page(s) will need a(n) _____ for quick identification, such as _____.

11. Certain special page layouts such as those for the _____, _____, or _____ allow an extra half-inch for the top margin.

12. The four basic components of a memorandum heading are (1) _____, (2)_____, (3)_____, and (4) _____.

13. A report that is bound on the left side should have the page numbers located in the _____, except for _____ pages where the numbers are _____.

14. Three main areas of information on the title page are (a) _____, (b) _____, and (c) _____.

15. Information about the identity of the authorizer should be preceded by the phrase _____, while the phrase _____ should precede the name of the writer.

16. The letters of transmittal and authorization should be typed in _____ format with the overall letter layout designed to take the shape of a(n) _____ corresponding to the proportions of the space in which it is typed.

17. Start typing the page containing the table of contents after spacing _____ down from the top, and below the title set up two _____ to give information on _____ and _____.

18. A title for a part of a report that serves somewhat like a headline for the part is called a(n) _____.

19. Two techniques used to make titles for report parts stand out from the text are use of _____ and use of _____.

Application Exercises

Exercise 1:   Take one of the memorandum cases given in your text at the end of Chapter 13 (your teacher will select one), and write it to conform to the appearance of Figure 20-10.

Exercise 2: Take the following outline you have developed as a guide to write the report. First, show how it would appear typed as a table of contents. (Make up page numbers.) Correct any errors you may find in the outline.

I. Orientation to the Problem
A. Authorization by Ms. Charlotte Kimberly
B. Feasibility Study for a New Bank in Port City
C. Survey of Local Residents and Businesses
D. Development of the Analysis

II. Analysis of Residential Responses
A. Economic Makeup of the Port City Area
1. Higher Income Areas in North and East Neutral
2. Medium and Lower Income Areas in South and West Positive
B. Probable Use of a New Bank by Individuals
1. Significant Differences by Neighborhood Income Status
2. Significant Differences by Age of Residential Neighborhood
C. Overview of Individual Responses

III. Analysis of Business Responses
A. Economic Profile of Port City Area Businesses
1. Wide Variety of Business Establishments
2. Most Businesses Medium or Small by Sales Volume
3. Growth Pattern in Area Business
B. Probable Use of a New Bank by Businesses
1. Retailing and Service Firms Most Responsive
2. Medium-size and Smaller Firms Most Positive
3. Newer Businesses Favorable
C. Overview of Business Responses

IV. Conclusions

Special Topic: Correctness of Communication

21

What sort of action would result in a sports game if one team played by football rules and the second played by soccer rules? The common rules of grammar and punctuation help make sure reader and writer are playing the same "communication game" so that the confusion of "miscommunication" resulting from each person following his or her own "rules" can be avoided.

Multiple Choice (Circle the best answer)

1. Correct use of punctuation, grammar, and spelling are important because:
    a. errors cause the reader to doubt the competence and efficiency of both the writer and the company he or she represents.
    b. errors create a negative reaction to the report or letter.
    c. errors detract from the content of the message.
    d. some errors cause misrepresentation of meaning and facts.
    e. all of the above.

2. Which of the following is correctly written?
    a. Employees writing techniques strongly affect the companys' image.
    b. Employees writing techniques strongly affect the company's image.
    c. Employees writing techniques strongly affect the companies' image.
    d. Employees' writing techniques strongly affect the company's image.
    e. Employees' writing techniques strongly affect the companies' image.

3. Words a writer inserts in a quotation should be set off with:
    a. single quotations.
    b. brackets.
    c. hyphens.
    d. italics.
    e. parentheses.

4. Commas serve a number of purposes. Select the following sentence correctly illustrating rule Cma 2.1 in your text:
    a. Good grammar, punctuation, and spelling can help your career goals.
    b. Good grammar punctuation and spelling can, help your career goals.
    c. Good grammar punctuation and spelling, can help your career goals.
    d. Your career goals can be helped by good grammar, punctuation and spelling.
    e. Getting the idea across, is, the main thing, really.

5. Principal clauses may be separated by:
    a. parentheses and/or commas.
    b. hyphens and/or semicolons.
    c. semicolons and/or dashes.
    d. commas and/or semicolons.
    e. coordinating conjunctions and/or quotation marks.

6. A principal clause:
   a. has a subject and verb.
   b. can stand by itself.
   c. may be connected with another principal clause by a coordinating conjunction preceded by a comma.
   d. may be separated from another related principal clause by a semicolon.
   e. all of the above.

7. In which of these sentences are commas correctly used?
   a. The report is due on March 16, 1993, in the Dayton, Ohio, office.
   b. The report is due on March 16, 1993 in the Dayton, Ohio office.
   c. However the report is not due in Dayton, Ohio until March 16.
   d. The report of course will be due on March 16 in Dayton, Ohio.
   e. The report however, is due on March 16th, 1993 in the Dayton, Ohio, office.

8. A dash:
   a. may be used for purposes of emphasis.
   b. may be used to show interrupted thought.
   c. should be typed by hitting the hyphen key twice without spacing.
   d. may be used to set off expressions using internal punctuation.
   e. all of the above.

9. Italics are used to identify:
   a. the title of a book or magazine.
   b. the title of a chapter in a book.
   c. the title of an article in a magazine.
   d. an exact quotation by a speaker or writer.
   e. a quotation within another quotation.

10. In a long quotation, a:
    a. series of five periods may be used to show words were omitted.
    b. series of eight periods may be used to show a paragraph was omitted.
    c. series of eight periods may be used to show a whole sentence was omitted.
    d. series of four periods may be used to show a whole sentence was omitted.
    e. whole line of periods is used to indicate a sentence has been left out.

11. To identify a quotation within a quotation, use:
    a. a second set of quotation marks.
    b. a set of single quotation marks.
    c. italics.
    d. a set of dashes.
    e. parentheses.

12. The appropriate relationship between quotation marks and other punctuation marks is shown in which of the following?
    a. "Will mortgage interest rates ever drop?" the woman asked.
    b. Who can answer "Whether Inflation Can Be Curbed"?
    c. "Some groups have a vested interest," Wilson responded, "in seeing that inflation continues."
    d. He said, "Economic prospects are frightening for the middle class"; and then he discussed seven points to back his thesis.
    e. all are correct.

13. Which of the following violates the rules for correct use of pronouns?
    a. After the teacher and Jim talked over the problem, he was still dissatisfied.
    b. After the teacher and Jim talked over the problems, they agreed to meet again.
    c. Carbon copies of the letter were sent to three of them.
    d. Whom did the committee select for the award?
    e. Each person should be careful that no one else can copy from his or her answer book to the exam.

14. In using numbers in a report, you need to:
    a. use Arabic numerals at all times.
    b. use the "rule of nine" at all times.
    c. spell out a number when it begins a sentence.
    d. spell out fractions and decimals.
    e. always present the days of the month in numerical form.

15. It is important to use the appropriate verb tense to identify place in time. Which of the following sentences fails to do this?
    a. Some coastal areas farther north actually have milder temperatures because of the influence of major ocean currents that moderate their climatic conditions.
    b. The choice of that particular site for the new plant was affected by the fact that mines that can supply raw ores were located nearby.
    c. In 1993, the newspaper editor endorsed the Independent candidate for office.
    d. The saleswoman said XYZ Corporation was one of her best customers because it had ordered more than $200,000 worth of merchandise from her company in the preceding quarter.
    e. We reported to the credit bureau that we have had trouble collecting from this account several times in the past six months.

Completion

1. Correctness is important because it carries the image of _____.

2. An apostrophe is used to _____ and/or to _____.

3. The appropriate punctuation mark to introduce a series or list of items (enumeration) or a quotation is a(n) _____.

4. Examples of coordinating conjunctions are _____, _____, _____, _____, and _____.

5. A nonrestrictive modifier is one that could be omitted from the sentence without _____ _____.

6. Words that interrupt the normal flow of a sentence often may be included correctly if set off by _____, rule number _____.

7. Nouns or adjectives in a series should be separated by _____.

8. The appropriate punctuation that should be used sparingly to express strong emotion is _____ _____.

9. An adverb not ending in "ly" should be joined to the adjective it modifies by a(n) _____.

10. Use periods correctly in expressing the following abbreviations: (a) Associate of Arts degree, (b) Bachelor of Business Administration, (c) Doctor of Medicine, (d) Organization of Petroleum Exporting Countries, (e) Equal Employment Opportunity Commission.

(a) _____, (b) _____, (c) _____,

(d) _____, (e) _____.

11. The title of an article in a magazine should be set off by _____.

12. If one or both of two independent clauses are long and/or contain commas, they should be separated by a(n) _____.

13. Nouns and pronouns are modified by _____; verbs and adjectives are modified by _____.

14. A singular noun or pronoun should be accompanied by a(n) _____ verb, while plural nouns or pronouns need a(n) _____ verb form.

15. If a modifying clause does not clearly belong with a word in a sentence, it is said to _____ and is unacceptable grammar.

Application Exercises

Exercise 1:

Part 1: Circle the misspelled words in the following list:

accept	collegiate	judgment	success
acheive	comunicate	knowledgeable	suitible
accountting	consede	liesure	syllable
affect	curiculum	material	thru
asign	dessert	narative	transister
beginning	dictionary	occurred	univercity
believe	dividend	personell	vehicle
beleaf	eccology	potatoe	volume
cancel	financialy	procede	whether
choose	immediately	questionaire	you're

Part 2: Distinguish between the following pairs of common homophones by using each correctly in a sentence:

1. ascent
   assent

2. been
   bin

3. board
   bored

4. break
   brake

5. buy
   by

6. calender
   calendar

7. coarse
   course

8. here
   hear

9. its
   it's

10. lessen
    lesson

11. principal
    principle

12. right
    write

13. site
    cite

14. stationery
    stationary

15. your
    you're

16. wait
    weight

Part 3: Distinguish between the following pairs of commonly confused words by using each correctly in a sentence.

1. affect
   effect

2. imply
   infer

3. among
   between

4. that
   which

5. can
   will

Exercise 2: Identify the grammatical, punctuation, and spelling errors in the following sentences. Use the "codes" given in the text—i.e., write "QM 1" to indicate that quotation marks are needed to enclose someone's exact words.

1. In the supervisors opinion, the rules about how employees use their coffee-break time is too lenient.

2. The report, on the Collins plant site, is on the managers desk.

3. The paneling comes in four finishes; mahogony, pine, birch, and oak.

4. If Jane Reynolds accepts the sales manager's job, and the vice president hopes she will, the staff probably will be reorganized.

5. Growth in production estimates for 1996-98. Figures are based on the governments economic projections to the year 2000.

6. Thirty two members attended the special workshop on Communication for Managers.

7. The article How to Dress for a Job Interview appeared in Monday's edition of The Daily Press.

8. Many students belong to collegiate chapters of ASPA, the American Society for Personnell Administrators.

9. Attendance by members at the rally were estimated at more than two hundred.

10. Proper usage of the rules of grammar are always important in projecting a positive image.

11. Long reports show a high degree of formality, require more appended parts, prefatory parts, and usually do not use personal pronouns.

12. When the teacher told the student what the assignment was, he said it would be due on Tuesday.

13. The data in the records surprised both I and her.

14. She did not know if the committee meeting was scheduled for 2 p.m. on Tuesday or Wednesday.

15. She said, The minutes of the comittee meeting are being typed by the secretary.

16. The president asked the sales manager what dates had been set for the promotion campaign?

17. According to the report, sales increased by 23 percent in repair parts, fourteen percent in accesories, and only eight percent in new automobiles.

18. The new developements caused President Browne to exclaim, We must learn to expect the unexpected.

19. I would like to order two dozen skirts, size 36, a dozen knit gloves size 7 1/2, and two dozen red ski socks, mixed sizes.

20. Neither of the salespeople were able to convince the production manager to increase scheduled production, he said ordered supplies made it possible.

21. The arid regions of the Southwest were ideal for current experiments involving growing guayle as a possible domestic source of rubber.

22. I hardly could believe the newpaper article entitled Bunny Thermal Units; it reported a nursery owner safes $25 a month in fuel costs, even after paying for the rabbits food, by using the body temperature [101°] of several dozen rabbits rather than relying only on gas to heat his greenhouses.

23. The semester ends the twentieth of December.

24. What do you think of using geese as part of our grounds security program asked the new security director. They have been used successful for this purpose by several other companies.

25. At first the idea seemed amusing, but in checking up on the suggestion, I found several examples of companies using geese as "watchdogs", "watch-geese", with considerable success.

26. We will try to honor whatever you and him agree on for a delivery date.

27. 1992 was one of the most momerable election years on record.

28. Over 3,000,000 people live in Puerto Rico.

Special Topic: Business Research Methods

22

Multiple Choice (Circle the best answer)

1. Which of the following sources would you not use in the direct approach to library research?
    a. Almanacs
    b. Encyclopedias
    c. Card catalog
    d. Biographical directory
    e. Government publications

2. The card catalog lists books by
    a. author and subject only.
    b. title only.
    c. author and title only.
    d. subject only.
    e. subject, author, and title.

3. Which of these sources would you not use in the indirect method of library research?
    a. A prepared bibliography
    b. The card catalog
    c. A database
    d. A periodical index
    e. A trade directory

4. Which of these methods is *not* a form of primary research?
    a. Search through company records
    b. Database searching
    c. Experimentation
    d. Observation
    e. Survey

5. The major shortcoming of the before-after design of experiment is that it:
    a. does not explain all of the change measured.
    b. is unnecessarily complex.
    c. takes more time than other designs.
    d. is more expensive than other designs.
    e. involves human bias.

6. Which of these steps are not involved in the controlled before-after design of experiment?
    a. Before measurements for both groups
    b. After measurements for both groups
    c. Averaging of measurements for leveling factor
    d. Selection of two comparable groups
    e. Introduction of experimental factor in one group only

7. A sample constructed by selecting every 10th person from a list of the people involved in the study is best classified as a:
   a. quota sample.
   b. random sample.
   c. stratified random sample.
   d. systematic sample.
   e. area sample.

8. The technique that is most likely to produce a sample with the proportionate makeup of the group under study is a:
   a. quota sample.
   b. random sample.
   c. stratified random sample.
   d. systematic sample.
   e. area sample.

9. Which of these questions is most in accord with the rules for questionnaire construction?
   a. Is Sprite your favorite soft drink?
   b. Do you drink soft drinks regularly?
   c. How much did your family spend on soft drinks last year?
   d. How do you buy soft drinks?
   e. How many soft drinks have you consumed in the past 24 hours?

10. Which of the rules for questionnaire construction is most likely to be violated by this question: "What was your overall grade-point average in college?"
    a. Avoid leading questions
    b. Seek facts
    c. Ask only what can be remembered
    d. Avoid questions that touch on personal pride or prejudice
    e. Make questions easy to understand

11. The technique of measuring a respondent's attitudes on a matter using number values on a scale is called:
    a. rating.
    b. ranking.
    c. positioning.
    d. pilot study.
    e. tabulating.

12. Electronic card catalog has advantages over the manual card catalog. Which of the following is not an advantage?
    a. The electronic catalog gives the searcher more categories on which the database can be searched.
    b. The elctronic catalog will always identify all the sources available when one searches for keywords in the title.
    c. The electronic catalog allows the searcher to restrict the search by applying various limitations.
    d. The electronic catalog retrieves sources faster than one could in a manual catalog.
    e. All of the above are advantages.

Completion

1. Research that uses information from printed sources is called _____.

2. _____ research uncovers information firsthand.

3. _____ libraries contain all kinds of materials whereas _____ libraries are limited to a few kinds.

4. Before preparing your own bibliography you should _____.

5. The major key to the resources of a library is the _____.

6. The most useful periodical index for most business research is the _____.

7. Library research using computers to find and retrieve information is called _____.

8. The experiment may be defined as a form of research in which you _____.

9. The experimental design involving selecting a test group, measuring a variable, introducing the experimental factor, and measuring again is called the _____.

10. An experimental design that accounts for influences other than the experimental factor is the _____ _____.

11. The premise that a sufficiently large number of items taken at random from the larger number of items in a group will have the characteristics of the group is called _____.

12. Simply stated, sample reliability means that the sample must be _____.

13. _____ requires that the sample selected have the characteristics of the group from which the sample is drawn.

14. In probability sampling all items in the population have a known probability of being selected. Four major types of probability sampling are (1) _____, (2) _____, (3) _____, and (4) _____.

15. In nonprobability sampling all items in the population have an unknown probability of being selected. Three major types of nonprobability sampling are (1) _____, (2) _____, and (3) _____.

16. The sampling technique that gives every member of the group under study an equal chance of being selected is _____.

17. _____ subdivides the group under study and makes random selections within each subgroup.

18. A leading question is one that _____.

19. To get information involving matters of pride or prejudice, one has to _____.

20. In asking only for information that can be remembered, one should consider the fundamental laws of memory:
(1) _____, (2) _____, and (3) _____.

21. Recording techniques that measure the intensity of a respondent's feelings are called _____. The two most common forms of it are _____ and _____.

22. You can get answers to a questionnaire in three ways: (1) _____,
    (2) _____, and (3) _____.

23. Before actually conducting a survey, it is wise to test your plan by conducting a _____.

Application Exercise

Select a hypothetical business organization and list two problems that it could solve by each of these techniques:
(1) observation, (2) experiment, (3) survey.